LOSING TIME

meditations of a broken heart

written and illustrated by

Kristina V. Kairyte

To JNM, my favourite ghost

Contents

endings

the end

acknowledgments

about the author

foreword

Stories are not merely invented. Stories happen. They happen upon us like the very defining factors of our existence, such as gravity or time. There is no heartbeat without a story. And some stories matter in our limited timelines so much that they refuse to pass quietly. They refuse to be laid to rest and die a calm, contented death, but remain spinning on their own axes like the earth itself, creating their own parallel lives, their own ecosystems of longing. Those are the stories that demand to be obsessed over until they are written and therefore appeased, for they now know they will live to be heard.

This story set up camp in my body, overcame the flow of my life and held it hostage until I agreed to put my pen to work. And when the pen finally lifted, peace was made, and time started running forwards again.

This story and the accompanying poetry were my daily affirmations when faced with events that felt much larger than me. They guided me on the narrative line towards absolution, and as such, are therapeutic and empowering in their nature. I hope they manage to light a sense of wonder in you the way they did in me.

beginnings

---◆---

the one where the inception of love
sits sharply in my memory

my lost lover

Let me narrate your way back into my heart. I hope you can find it again despite the surrounding darkness that has been whispering emptiness and rippling with the breathlessness of anxiety. Like Scheherazade, clutching onto the lifeline that is your attention, I will recount to you the most visited version of my pain. Its cool breath on my face reminds me that you are out there, in the world where skyscrapers grow on deserts, where days repeat themselves, and hope, directed at others, echoes in the sticky heat, perpetually unable to live its own meaning. You will find me at the tipping point of the blade where the persistent hands of the clock turn the bitterness of your desire into anger.

When you come, I will wrap you in the blanket of my longing. We will hide under it like two innocents, years before I stifled my love for you, before I betrayed your kindness with blunt accusations disguised as the truth, before you promised to love another. Before feeling wildly unprepared for it you had the first fruit of this love. You will look into my eyes, and you will fall into the depth of my emotion. You will take a break from beheading our memories because you will hear the weight of my words within the cracks in my voice. My tears will start flowing out of your eyes as we share this communion of our love that now rests in the crumbs of time.

Numb with helpless determination, you will follow me to nameless hotel rooms in nameless cities. We will build pillow forts and demolish them with the careless limbs of the bodies in the throes of lovemaking. You will bend into me and drink my story until your own life starts causing you pain. You will hate me for this taste of primordial knowledge, rustling in the leaves of frost-bitten apple trees. But you will love me too for I will still be there, unchanged.

Slowly, you will come to realise that I am the villain. I am the reason you do not kiss your wife like before, when you still harboured hope of forgetting me. I am not a blushing girl with a downcast gaze in the presence of her beloved. I am an evil woman, writing to her lost lover, stretching her pain to reach him, poisoning his new life with visions from the old one. Grief is inherently selfish, it hungers for your sanity, and I have been stuck in the cycle of despair for so long that I have become it. I am the weaver of pain; night is where I store my daggers.

We should have stopped this spindle when we could still step back into life together. But we held onto our pride and distrust, and now the narrative is ahead of us, and time matters no more. We are living in the unrecorded moments before the sand clock is turned over again to flow for a new story to its inevitable demise. We will wreck each other's lifelines until there is nothing left standing. Until we are able to see each other again, naked in honesty like on the first day of humanity, surrounded by the shredded tapestries of our hastily constructed lives.

Even now, I still wake up when the night is deep because the sun is rising where you are, and you are thinking of me. You told me once when I was conjuring our future that you too wake up from arcane dreams that make your manhood pulsate to my heartbeat. No time or distance has changed that. Not even my betrayal, not even you, promising in front of God and society to love and care for another woman. We pushed each other away, resenting the unwelcome pangs of kindness we still felt towards one another. Ignoring the complicated mesh of rage and desire storming our insides, we punished each other with silence. The silence felt heavier every day in the company of the ignorant, so we started growling at each other to remind us of our voices. And now, we are back to talking, loving, whispering impossible hope through the cracks in our pride, stretching the membrane of time and space to allow us to share one more moment together.

So, let me tell you a story. Because tonight I am hurting, and I need you to listen. Tonight, I need you to see me again.

after the vision of your eyes

i stumbled over your eyes
and fell into the universe
backwards
into the winged darkness
rocked
by water-light soundwaves

        my skin sighed
        as it touched the surface
        of liquid pleasure

smooth
like kitten-heels
snuggling up with stockings
velvet
brushing against the cocktail hand
backless strings
holding heart in fabric
and the railing
purring with delight
pulling skin in
to tip
over the dream

hanging at the bottom of the well
lays my room
a square pool with stars
held
in the magnetic hum of your pupils

and i realise now
how deep a moment can be
how it draws you in to idolise
the process of falling
how it sets you up to forgive
its saccharine ways
as it lazily stretches
across time
and into infinity

you came to me
with a ring

Dubai, 2017

Cars line up on a lazy road at sunrise, pleading grace from the traffic lights. I listen to them from the heights of my hotel room. It's five a.m. Suddenly, it's already six. Time moves like in a zoetrope[1], playing on

---

1 Zoetrope is an optical toy from pre-cinema days in the 19th century, playing on the brain's ability to retain an image for a fraction of a second after it is gone, this way creating an illusion of continuous movement. In scientific experimentation this phenomenon was called the 'persistence of vision'.

my eyes with the persistence of images. I want to force the sounds and visions into my head. They float behind my eyelids, distracting me from sleep. Seeing you has always felt like a once in a lifetime event no matter how many times I am back to experience it. I must record the details – the sand dust on the street, the cringing shadows on the metro station walls – because I will not be allowed to hold these memories. The time will steal away the anxious bliss I feel waiting for you.

But what if you won't come? Tonight, this question has been whispered dreamlessly to me in an uncountable number of ways. My cosy, faithful fears have found their voices through the uncertainty of your presence. I imagine watching you from the distance as you approach my road and the fear crumbles my vision, blowing you to dust.

Seven a.m. You are only getting up now, keeping yourself preoccupied with the morning chores, making coffee with one hand, and rocking your new-born in the other. Relying on the routine to ground you and drown out the nervous excitement of taking the unsupervised turn and finding me there. Your mind is speeding in front of you. Too early, push it down, steady your lip corners – they cannot yet rise with timid hope.

You did not kiss your wife goodbye, but she did not ask for it either.

The call to prayer rises through the slumber. It encourages me to open the curtains and watch the morning sun, charging forward from behind the skyscrapers that pierce the shroud of dust with their sharp reflections. They look invincible but their shape quivers in the heat. A man cycles towards the Burjuman metro station and I get distracted, wondering how he is able to do it so effortlessly under the weight of this eternal summer. Every day here looks as the one before and so he cycles forever in the glass globe of my memory.

I take a moment to allow myself to feel small in this city of five-lane roads, hundred-floor constructions, and infinity of sand grains. They roam the groomed surfaces, insulting the city's efforts to rise above the desert. They travel in our shoes, shifting between our stories, scaling our windows to determine the size of our existence until the pulsating traffic pulls them back in.

No one will remember me here. There is too much structure in their lives to pay attention to a lonely traveller, too much healthy chatter to distract them from my quiet shape. Seeing myself out of focus in the corners of their eyes, I get worried that my dreamy presence in this world will disappear, and so I take a picture to capture my heartbeat against the horizon. The camera focuses on the little sand waves on my windowpane, terrified of their imminent fall.

The knock comes earlier than expected and my heart sprints to the door before I get up to step softly behind it. I did not prepare for you; I did not even brush my hair, and the clothes I have on you have seen before. I used to dress up for you every day just to give you the refreshed sensation of meeting me anew but with a comforting intimate undercurrent of my skin.

Who is that stranger that my heart pulls towards?

Today, I want you to see me as I am, true to your memory of the sleep-glazed eyes, the morning breath, the soft arm hair, and the smell of warm skin, kissed by the sun. You have come to claim back my heart and I want you to be overcome by its familiarity.

The moment you stepped through the door, your eyes locked with mine. We stumbled across the room – two imperfect people, sucked into each other's galaxies of longing. You moved your hand to touch me, and I saw it: a thick gold wedding band. You came to me with your wedding ring on.

You thought this made you honest.

The ring was the wrong fit. Or maybe you shrunk once you put it on. It was falling off your ring finger, so you had to move it to the middle one instead. It is as if this memento of your vow was telling you it wanted nothing to do with the arrangement.

There, on the wrong finger, it had grown into your skin, rooted in its warmth. It was the closest thing to you, and I wished to become it. Even before opening the door, I had had to live through the imminent goodbye while still aching to be yours. You would leave, but I shall deposit my soul into you, and you would not leave alone.

To you, the ring was a technicality, just like your wedding itself. It should not offend me. It was just a tick-box, an indicator of your status in life. For me, it was a question of the heart. Later, we would have conversations about what it meant for you to say yes to another woman, to write your vows, to choose the song you would be walking down the aisle to. You did not do any of those things. You chose your suit and that was the extent of the effort you put into the day you declared your dedication to this woman, who graciously came to breathe into you a spark of new life. I wanted to hear that the sacrament you performed was unsacred. You did it like an actor, learning the lines and voicing them with relief that you would never be asked to say them again. Looking down on you with the crushing righteousness of the just, declared such by their suffering, I wanted to say to you: "There is nothing holy about your matrimony".

But you were never flashy or loud about your love. You dreamed small to make sure you could always be satisfied. Your love – unglamorous and undemanding – could be trusted in the plain everyday. You had become a better man for her because you had gone through me. I lost you but the pain of it has grown you.

Two years later, I could look into your soul again in this shabby hotel room. You had no words, and the city had no memory to contain them.

13

before
responsibility

your life before responsibility
was a life before knowledge
of freedom

> you knew the boundaries
> you loved to break them
> secretly
> without giving it any meaning

your happiness
was inconspicuous
when you kissed
another long-legged girlfriend
under the moonlight
air swollen with the buzz
of the big city

you knew
it was just for the time being
as there was a lot
expected from you

you ran like an athlete
the fact your father was proud of
this enviable achievement

or an escape route

for your immodest desires
quietly pressed
into uncertain shadows
under the dome
of your home

but you only discussed
papers and grades
and carefully nothing else

and you also went rogue
in the playful standoff
with your brothers
a pack of puppies in a tumble
careless with matches

these little men

who believed they knew
the mechanics of this world
proudly winding time
ahead of their frustrations

so stubbornly sure were they
of their footing
that they forgot to watch out
for the fall

and there I was
like an axis in your timeline
a page marker

or a page turner

a book
at the time when
you only meant it
to be a sentence

and you knew how to read me
but you got scared
seeing the word transform and grow
like a living thing
not knowing where it ends
not being able
to skip ahead and see
whether it holds the promised freedom -

an immeasurable expanse
that could be your future
thick with oxygen
almost too much to bear

drifting into the jungle

London, 2014-2017

In a different hotel room three years ago on a sweltering autumn day, you waited for me to come and love the distance away. Brushing off the lonely months like sawdust, you anchored us here - a solitary raft, strung from a couple of dusty suitcases, stuffed with clothes that made us feel foreign to ourselves.

Years passed and our love continued to be described in absences: your siblings could not know, your parents could not suspect, even your friends could not sense your unorthodox predilection. You were afraid of instating me into your world, building me up with words of commitment into a solid shape, edges sharpened by determination, bearing weight and therefore able to carry significance. And so, to prepare for the worst, I started slowly freezing my heart, stealing it back from you sinew by sinew and throwing these tired residues of affection to other lovers. To lose you by my own choice felt safer than handing you the power to abandon.

Our raft shook and split into two. You were pulled ahead by the currents to speed uncontrollably through your life. Meanwhile, I drifted into the jungle. The green was so deep it slowed time, thick with meanings of lost moments. It bore a deceitful silence: the apparent peace it held grew inconspicuously loud once you focused on it, reminding you that every leaf hides eyes to watch for your weakness.

In the jungle we all hunt and we are all hunted.[2]

Stuffy with temptation, the heat stretched skin around my bones in a new, suggestive fashion. And all of a sudden, I knew I was lusted. In this ecosystem of starved desire, I struggled to reach for your memory. Instead, I disappeared into the new rituals of longing.

You did not fight for me. You watched me, paralysed by the feeling of your inconsequence. You could not feel the weight of your being and thought that if you moved your muscles to grab my hand and pull me back, the air would slow and solidify, resisting this action. Although you were bound by the physics of this world, you thought that the world would refuse to validate you in it. Tradition was what moved matter. Your future was crafted a long time ago and you were told what it would be.

---

2 a line from Netflix's *Mawgli: Legend of the Jungle* (2018), spoken by Baloo to Mawgli when teaching him about the laws of the jungle

You felt that if your soul left your chest and there would only be a shell of your body roaming through your days, life would continue as it had always done, ignorant of this change. It would flow effortlessly independent of your decisions. You were just sorry that even in this state of capitulation you still got hurt.

When my love ricocheted back, crashing into me with the force of sudden remembering, it was too late. You allowed me back in for a mere four days. I visited your world of searing sunrises and dreamy afternoons, but I could not heal the wounds with my hands – the same tools that tore your flesh open. You were steadier, more rational than me, and you wanted to believe that you had a chance to love again. But what was love? You dedicated yourself to the love of your family and allowed yourself to kiss a steady, rational girl your mother had found for you. You told me you enjoyed it while I begged you not to choose her. Encouraged by the dizzying sense of rogue independence you went back to her again and again, light with the blessings of the world.

You did not tell me about her to hurt me, you were just being honest. Hovering in the margins of your life, I found myself watching you fall in love with the idea of her in the few short weeks before your wedding. You had discovered the jungle yourself, and the humming of desire pulled at your focus. I had nothing else to offer, no promises to make that I had not already broken.

On the day of your wedding, the church bells tolled in the background, and the wind rolled the sound into my hair, spreading the strands over the wild grass blades. I lay as if outside of myself, eyes open, dead to the world, as rushes passed the echo across the swamps and rivers on their tender swaying shoulders. This loud silence was void of life. Space felt elastic but time was solid. I tripped over the enormity of this moment and plummeted deep into myself. Cloaked with the spongy sense of apathy, I could not feel the impact yet.

When I was three, I felt hypnotised by scissors. Whenever I would see them, I would reach towards them slowly, respectfully, like they had a great power I was craving to possess. Once in my hands, I would cut everything around me with the same respectful wonder, slowly tearing through the sheets I was sitting on. I would then observe my work and touch my hands in awe of their newfound talent to destroy.

On the eve of your wedding, I went down the corridor to the room of another man in the hand-embroidered nightgown you gifted me. Wrapped in the cloth of traditions and wifehood, I consecrated our love in hopes that this act would stop it from counting in my suddenly imbalanced existence. You see, it is a special kind of hell watching your pain being exiled for the inconvenience that it is to others. Nobody wants to see it, let alone engage with it. Rattling with hollow despair, it echoes like a pebble in a rusty can, floating down a slow green river, alone and anchorless.

Now, your wedding anniversary will also always mark my fall. I pushed out my love for you in order to commit an act of self-denial in a careless somersault over the rocks. Revenge was a form of self-destruction, and the following months stretched barren with solitude.

Your only request was for me to allow you to be happy. Each time you called you said it was the last. You raged at me for your inexplicable need to hear my voice, for my sorrow to seep through the sound waves and envelop you. I pulled back from you and tried to slow time into a lethargic trickle, but I found that I could not make myself disappear.

I am forever here now.

My nerve endings push deeper into your scent as bodies never forget. I tiptoe in the shadows of your living room until you choose to see me. Once I used cars and planes to reach you but now, I must walk this distance in quiet pilgrimage. I am learning to find solace in the slow signs of my progress.

Before you sneak out of my room, your hand brushes against my cheek like a whispered apology and my voice falls back into my throat with an echo. You leave nothing behind. Before I check out of the hotel, I lie on our sheets swimming amongst our beheaded senses in a painfully blue world. When I finally leave, I smuggle out the traces of you on my skin.

that summer

Abu Dhabi, 2012

eyes wide with childlike wonder

                    i turn to you

what gifts will you bestow upon me
Abu Dhabi

                Allah Akbar

born in dreamy towers
lifting up like dust

a dome of overpowering peace
sliding off the glass walls
and into your palms
dry and warm

palm-shaped shadows
embroidering the sand
receiving burnt footsteps
on the pastel desert
guarding you
while you carry me over the waves
to more complacent waters

a honeycomb airport
carefully unfamiliar
withholding the first heatwave
from hopeful travellers
swarming out to build
a life
that is comfortably foreign

white car tents
reflecting a cooling halo
you feel entitled to step into
is this your car sir

                              it is not

and you return dreams
keeping the aftertaste of want
as white as on your first day

a gold bar ATM
showcasing your worth
dispensing your value
in a carpeted foyer

                                    artificial light
                                    soft padded walls

a trophy for your vanity

                                    you

parting the busy road
your back on me
but your soul facing
your arms
never touching me
until the shadows stretch
the length of your kitchen

did i come to you by chance

                                    i entered your life

like the very first woman
a flower-patterned dress
covering me
from the wandering looks
questioning gazes

                                    curious eyebrows

is she with you what's the secret

eyes unafraid

                                    they know not to stop looking

following to a seat
on a bus
next to a woman
defiantly disinterested
shielded by her ancestral robe
guarded by her Tradition

                    they look at the colour of my hair
                    and my garment beckons

you unwrap me like a gift
that does not belong in this foggy heat
and seethed through edgy shadows
the vision meets its maker

we held each other
to make sure we were real

your father's friend
a neighbour
marches towards me
miss Europe miss England
you descend
from the building to save me

                    worrying
                    that your father will hear of this

                    he will hear
                    of the wilted flower-patterned sheets
                    and a girl underneath them

humming lightly to the tune of the fan

and her feigning ecstasy

on the bed
he made his dreams on

he will hear

of the laces caressing the breeze
laundry hung for all to witness
a pale face watching
the neighbourhood come to life

the neighbourhood he chose
to craft his dreams in

he will hear

of the water triple-boiled and frozen
to satisfy eager mouths
that reach for it but meet
distracted half-way

the water he prepared
to nourish your dreams on

he will hear

of your mother's jewellery box
now touched by curious hands
she did not invite

the box she brought with her
to rest her dreams in

he will hear

of the sofa leather
supporting healthy breasts

        they bounce

as you sit to distract
the girl from reading

he lay there too
crushed by his dreams

        he will hear

of her wiping your sweat
from your forehead
in careful motion

        eyes proud

on the street
for all taxis to see

the street he planted
his tender-stemmed life on

        he will hear

of the curries frozen
out of care for one
that two were feasting on

the curries that were made
to feed your dreams to grow

two hearts said grace
but only one grace mattered

he did not hear a thing

we rushed

past the fish markets
to the boats on the docks

to share our heritage
to extinguish the daylight

feasting on water
Eid Mubarak
the bow of the ship dipped
in the drowning sun

we measured our desire
by the time spent in malls
gazing at the elevator ceiling

and the old men

leaning over slender girls

kissed
by turmeric milk lips

hailing the mysteries
of gold-cold hotel rooms

we roamed

in the empty Louvre
unfinished galleries
imagining the future
imagining the past

that absence of history

we built our dreams on

we took

pictures of toilet door figurines
bilingual street signs
to remember
the mood of our walks
where samovars only tipped

in our favour

we dropped to the knees
at hurried churches
with fanning families
winding down outside
soaking drops of light
from uncollected blessings

we hoped

they would suffice

we passed

the round-table men
the white slipper men
the wife-beater men

watchful
playing cards twice daily
guarding the entrance

challenging our fear

we walked

in the white mosque
uplifted by white space

encouraged by white walls

blinded by white light
bathing in white wonder
ceramic flowers
reflecting your laughter

we greeted

little birds that carried
little prayers
and reached
for fallen dates
to lift them up again

injured by the sun

hurt

we lay together

we watched

the handles of the clock
in silent terror
and hid them in the sand

the henna woman saw it

and yawned

your jeans were too tight
to disembark the camel
i was too light
to surf the dunes

                    so we met

at the shisha table
to puff our worries up in smoke

we gazed at the stars
and for a moment
we knew we existed

                    we hurried

to the end

the car naming ceremony

Abu Dhabi, 2017

I took a bus to your city. Four hours on the road just to be able to see you for one. Buses here have been reserved for the poor and the cost for getting onto one is merely symbolic. But the truly poor are invisible here. Public transport carries the more general public now: an African woman in flip flops, loud on her phone; an Arab man, silent and considerate as he lets me pass in front of him in the ticket queue; an Indian woman with her son and some seedlings, her kameez boldly bright and thick with comfort. There was a heavy jingle to her step which pulled the street towards her as she shuffled on with her burden, perfectly grounded, the axis of this little universe.

The shadows tilted on the bus terminal wall, pulling down the residue of the day, stripping away the sharpness of heat to make space for a kinder, slower evening. The familiar fear of knowing your face again settled in lazily like a cat, finally content as it tasted the early signs of nature's relief in the air.

You had it all planned out. As moments were ticking by, you drove us to a remote beach, far away from everyone who knew you. They owned your life, and you would not be able to escape the plague of inquisitive tongues should they see you in the company of an unfamiliar woman. Hiding was not new to us but now it bore a different set of consequences.

The beach was full of families who came out to enjoy the outdoors after a long and scorching summer. I wondered how you felt when your wife went into labour in fifty-degree heat. I knew you were ready; you always were when it came to others, and yet I wondered about your emotions – something you tended to quietly push aside. It went well, and you thanked God heartily for this enormous blessing of holding a taste of relief, even if for a moment.

We sat in your car surrounded by silence, overwhelmed and unable to speak. Outside, a woman argued through her battoulah[3] with the traffic guards, her words carving out new laws for her land. Kids screamed gleefully chasing an inflatable ball, and the passers-by glanced at us with an entitled curiosity. This was our first meeting in secret.

I explored the skin on your arms, carefully looking for signs of familiarity. They were there, the little freckles and stains, a minuscule scar you did not know you had, one hair bending at a stubborn angle. Worried about my preoccupied silence, you started to talk but soon gave up, distracted by my eyes. We drank each other's presence to heal ourselves and, in the end, we were able to say, "see you soon". We did not have a "goodbye" to give. Our goodbyes were always flesh-made, they required a sacrifice.

I wanted to know the name of your car and you laughed:

"It does not have a name, not like my previous one. When I was with you, I felt like a crazy man, I could believe in anything! Objects were

---

3   metallic face covering worn by Arab Muslim women, traditional to the Persian Gulf region

meaningful enough to hold names then".

You named your first car Esmeralda. I teased you when you told me because you wanted it to be a lover's car, your surrogate woman to surround you with tranquillity so that your mind could unfold in the privacy of her embrace. Such an object deserved a name. It was a second-hand car – a shame in a first-hand country where taxi drivers wear designer rings. But to me it was a solace, our own private world that moved across the desert to a hot springs oasis while we lunched at eighty miles an hour.

I was sad to hear you sold it to someone who was a stranger to these fantasies. But you long desired a new car, and you allowed yourself to get it when you got married. This car was big, it reflected your new status. New job, new wheels, new wife. A new man emerged, and Esmeralda was abandoned, her leather solace given away to other bodies with different definitions of joy.

"Well then, we will have to have a car naming ceremony", I said.

You laughed, and so the next day we initiated the new car into our nameless accomplice.

the home spirit

I fit into the tapestry of that crammed spare room in your house where you keep things away from your wife. A small window invites dusty light onto old wood and busy wallpaper, cradling your inconvenient past in its tired folds. The selective past that you are forbidden to remember yet unwilling to forget. Your sports trophies, your cigars you did not get to smoke after sex and the bottle of scotch you never finished. Now you are only allowed water and light beer on occasion.

And me.

Quietly, at nights when Manchester United is playing, you turn the volume up to free yourself. You touch the walls and breathe my name to summon me. I sit with you and place my hand on your thigh while you soar and crash with the heaves of the crowd on the screen. No words are ever spoken. Words are for her, for she is amongst the living. She has been granted the right to respond.

I am your home spirit. Obedient and patient.

When your passions are packed up and stored, she comes to check that they will not spill over. She opens the door wide, confident, as tucked under her belt she holds the keys to every cupboard, dresser, and cellar in this house. But she cannot notice me as my presence lines the room like last year's perfume on the cuffs of your wedding shirt. She too must breathe me in if she wants to gain entrance.

When the living sacrifice themselves to a memory, they give their flesh away. Time and distance lose their definitions as we call upon our past to take charge. The shadow you have become drifts away, deeper into your body to disappear as there is no space left for it amongst the sprawling roots of the past. The present you are not living cannot be sentenced to memory.

Do you feel my hand on your crotch when you are having dinner with your family? Can you sense me wandering the corridors? Sometimes you stop next to me, lightyears away, pulled into an island of serenity. Distracted by a voice that calls when you are alone, a touch that melts into your being. The spirit, sliding through your life like you did not create any walls, patiently sitting on your couch while you argue with your wife, playing with your child, making your glassware hum.

Remaining unseen.

In the room where I fit into the tapestry, amongst the greyed-out flowers with wilted thorns, you find me naked every time. And when you leave, you lock the door. To save yourself, you trap me in there, condemned to stay.

a see-through woman

London, 2018

a see-through woman wonders
from home to work
and work to home
pushed
between two points of meaning
like a bead on the abacus
perpetually
erasing her own progress

a see-through woman
left behind the point of acceleration

        is blown to dust

and disperses
in the underground's deafening speed
softly

brushing against the tired crowd

a see-through woman
cannot see her hand
and handles
the terror of surging under-exposure

> in a crowded world
> quietly

like a grown-up

a see-through woman
has warm skin
moving with her breath
up and down
and white window light
on morning curls on weekends

she grows herself out like a lizard

> with a hunger
> for someone to touch her

to meet the body's resistance
propelling her back
into existence
and when none comes
what else is left
but a straight face

sleepy life

Exeter, 2011-2012

You stood by the train door, unmoved by thorns begging by your window in a cloud of soft-falling pink petals. Your red t-shirt hung loosely from your shoulders and your short black hair lay unnaturally sleek, announcing your efforts at grooming. You looked genuinely amazed at this moment of fate: meeting this cute girl twice the same week.

I was not that girl.

You met Sara at a café in the Queen's building. I do not know what an accounting student was doing in the College of Humanities. It was not known as a social hub but maybe you were seeking something different, exploring new campus corners, looking for conversations but never daring to initiate them. Your eyes met those of an olive-skinned Italian with a head full of thick black curls. She kept your gaze locked to the point when she had to twist her neck to maintain the contact. True to the moment, she decided to come back and share a coffee with you.

We huddled together, making light conversation while the train charged forward, rocking the loud student crowd. I struggled to understand what you were saying as both of us were weighed down by our accents. *A Russian? A Pole?* People could never tell which one of the insignificant nations I was here to represent while they immediately knew yours: an Indian with a round belly, sharp elbows and a well-calculated dream. You touched your nose a lot, self-conscious of your difference. I could relate to that - I turned away when I smiled, feeling a little too mediocre. Sara was the only one here content with being herself. Your eyes had a liquid metal glimmer, simmering in between the warm browns. You seemed genuinely excited about this moment, and instead of worrying about how you saw me, I concentrated on listening.

We walked on the sand, pointing at the rocks, the sea, the chipped white houses like we were in a magical snow globe. We talked but we did not understand much. We needed practice using the language we did not feel fluent in to express the richness of our confused joy. You pulled me out of a shallow sea pool, and I said something about this being the warmest September I had ever lived through. The leaves were already yellow back home. You told me that where you are from, shadows are too thin to protect you and you roam indoors until evening falls like a sheet, expelling sighs of relief from concrete walls. We fell silent, captivated by visions of the worlds we suddenly desired.

I tried not to pay too much attention to you. I did not trust boys and I did not think you would stick around, yet I agreed for Sara to invite you for dinner. My insecurities, resulting in me always expecting the worst, should not affect her joy of making a friend. You cancelled at the last minute, and I felt that that was the end of our time together, but Sara invited you again without hesitation. To my surprise, this time you showed up. You spent an evening in the company of two girls, pasta, and wine. You left the stalling awkwardness at the door with your worn-in black sneakers and immersed yourself into our careless dinner games and dish washing rituals. You watched football with your mates and listened to Sven's overconfident opinions, yet you were also one of us now and you grew to be protective of this status.

But something must have changed. You must have touched me - slid your hand across mine or grabbed me mid-move to steady me - because one day I woke up craving for more. I created situations where my humour would be rewarded by you slipping into your closely guarded laughter, or where intrigued by my silences you would lean in for my touch. I would close my eyes and let the tingly-toed desire reach towards you - mere inches apart, drowned in oceans of dizzy space. You did not trust the competency of these senses, yet you gave in to them all the same.

I wove a tale to draw you in.

I got to know your darker instincts as well as your caring side. You would not walk away from a girl in need. And so, you walked at 2 a.m. to my flat to ward off sudden pangs of sleeplessness. You knew I had a friend next door, yet we hid this thought to preserve the innocence of our excuse. You would step into my bed, carefully wrapping yourself around this warm bundle of mellow desire, wondering how you ended up here. The moment I lay my head on your chest, my blood would become restless, and sleep would evade me all the same. Little did I know that your blood was also clawing at your skin where it touched mine. One day, overwhelmed by unconscious tension, you kissed me in your sleep, clumsily, mouth caressing its way up the chin until it reached my lips. I awoke and wrapped my legs around you. You did not yet know that I knew.

Eventually, we had to speak about it. You had Traditions passed on for you to care for and they did not like being pushed aside. Your gut whispered warnings in bodiless papery voices, familiar in their gripping authority. Yet I was a dreamer, I knew the taste of the fall, and to help you I gave a promise designed to be broken. We were not to sleep together again. We spent a moment to allow the innocence of our young love to peek through: when we said 'sleep', it meant exactly just that.

Two days apart were all we could manage. You called me as I was walking to a lecture. You said you were sleepy and had a headache. All this English winter wind was doing you no good. You also had an imaginary chocolate mousse as a decoy which should compel this imaginary girl with imaginary desires. I told you off, reminded you that you were not supposed to tempt me. You fell silent, momentarily weighed down by the guilt of the elder one. I walked to your place anyway, quicker than I would usually, skin taunt with anticipation.

We sat in your room, sipping tea and watching a squirrel dig for hidden treasures in the shadows of an ancient pine just outside your window. Garden Hill was beautiful, and you lifted me onto your knees so that I could see it better. I showed you how Tchaikovsky played by orchestra sounds like in the grey afternoon just before Christmas while you showed me how the first kiss frozen mid-air drips into my stomach. You carried me across your room and placed me onto the bed, your movements slow and heavy with care.

"I guess we are dating then," I whispered, smouldering at the edges.

We watched the darkness creep into the room as we lay side by side speechless. We could not feel the time; no time had passed but the night had fallen.

It was adorable to watch you act on the truths I already knew. You would later learn how sharp my senses really were. Sometimes, I would pull you out of hiding to make you face your words. Sometimes, I would let you lie. Sometimes, the truth was the wrong kind of cure.

From then on, we spent all our time together. I would meet you after your football practice, when you would be dripping with sweat, and make you kiss me before you washed the fight off. You sat patiently through long evenings while we stuffed chickens and baked our own winter myths, adapted for a snowless place. You watched us lovingly, waiting for the moment when I would put down the plates and lead you away behind the closed doors, your sour cream goddess in bread crumb surrender. At nights, you would wake up to fix my nightgown, touching your way through darkness under the sheets, savouring the textures of affection in our otherwise plain bed. Once satisfied with your work, you would hug me again and fall back asleep. You made care for me your joyful duty.

On Valentine's, we watched our life in Devon in the film *War Horse*, pointing at the screen and whispering: "Look, we live in a fairy tale!" That evening, you had little but you gave me your all. Your care extended to every part of my life, from dry socks to plentiful dinners. I would sit on your knees, sharing one plate of food, eaten with a single spoon between the two of us, and feel devoted to you. When I was flying home penniless, you opened your wallet and gave me its contents – a £20 note. I had breakfast at the airport, bathed in your lingering kindness.

It felt like you walked behind me, catching my footsteps.

You withstood the dinner parties at Sara's and the game of Jonathan-town with quiet patience. We drew Exeter on your belly, memorising the paths to places we loved and conjuring them up from your navel. You thought we were taunting you. We were merely telling you how inherent you were to our experience of the geography of this place. When you left, you took it all away with you, engraved on your skin, and left us feeling suddenly homeless.

Jobs, degrees, futures – it all meant nothing if they did not bring us closer together. The spring came and we started feeling uneasy. We only had a few more months left. I looked for a job to make us last the summer and you looked for a job to make us last a lifetime. You needed a visa to stay.

Once the summer came, we moved in together and played house in Rowancroft. We lived in amazing synchrony, sharing clothes, sharing meals, creating rituals to release our excitement, stored up through brief periods of separation. Carried away, we would stumble into the bathroom and collapse into a steaming old tub, marked with cracks and stains. I rested in between your legs, sipping wine, getting drunk on your presence. Each evening we would go to bed like newlyweds, excited like we had not yet seen our bodies bend and slip through curving shadows. I would watch you through the window of our tower coming back with nothing but bottled milk. Later, we would demolish the innocence of this image by gulping down the milk while our fingers wandered our bodies: unwrapped for each other and unapologetic.

We marvelled at small gestures of kindness, unable to afford bigger feats. I took you to the beach with an unclaimed £20 note I had found by The Black Horse pub. We walked in the rare sunshine, dizzy with life. Later, we swayed to the sounds of a jazz band, too amateur to dance yet unwilling to let go. We had grown to look so alike in our manners and gestures we could have been twins. You guarded me closely, handing to me the best companionship you could offer.

When I went back home in July, you took me to the train station. You laughed at my attempt to wear every single piece of clothing I was taking with me in order to save on check-in luggage. This became the image you would remember me by, together with the one where I grimace at the smell of your cologne. You were always on a mission to extract the truth from me, to sense doubts if there were any, but the truth of adoration hiding in such moments always caught you off guard.

You protected me so diligently that nobody knew of me: your gingerbread fairy with a cloud of blonde hair. I could have been imagined. Even your brothers found out only years later when you needed their help - you stood naked in trust, betrayed all the same. To your friends you announced only days earlier, their faces whirlpools of surprise, scepticism and awe at the impossible. And when the weekly hour came to speak with your parents, you would ask me to leave the room. You apologised but did not feel you could make it better. I obliged. We still had all the time in the world then.

You left at the end of the summer. I saw my dream start to slip away the moment you boarded the bus to Heathrow. On the bus stand, waiting for you to leave, unable to stop you, I cried so hard my body convulsed. You watched through the window perplexed: how could anyone be hurting for you so much? When the bus moved, I bolted after it. This bus held destiny. If it stopped, you would never leave.

The bus sped up and disappeared in the distance.

You would be back, but those short moments of bliss would only deepen the despair. The slowly dripping awareness carved black pools in my mind. Later, I would be drowning in them, and they would pour out of me at unexpected moments, making my vision stumble and my reason weaken.

You came from the people who knew their roots. They felt proud of their dedication to effortfully remember. Roots had to be given sacrifices. They grew to break through the feeble soil and to bind themselves into rituals. They required your own parents to bleed you on their altar until you had the right balance of life to please the narrative. Your life only came easy if you allowed yourself to get entangled in their steady convictions. But first, you had to learn to be happy in a world with lower sky and closer walls, where structure was both confinement and freedom from fight, worry and endless pursuit of self. It was for your own wellbeing; they drained you in order to train you.

I crossed two bridges and a train track on my way to work each morning. There were many windy days. Life was testing me.

losing time

Exeter, 2013-2014

"when the first man and the first woman
were banished from their home
time
was also set loose upon the world"[4]

---

4   from Aminata Forna's *The Devil That Danced On The Water*

i groomed a Devil in me

                    whole and new

it spoke from the ashes
like the smouldering night
nipping at my footsteps

the god of loss
hooves and horns

                    and sharp edges

risen to remind me of time
wasting its beat
by my slow feet

                    and to the supernaturals
                    we listen

how can you know
he is the one if you
have not known life
with anybody else

                    in an instant

the ticking sound of the clock
took over and my happiness
could only exist
in comparison
to someone else's

                    the prophet of doubt

the watchmaker with arthritic fingers
he took a tape measure

and wrapped my tongue
to discover
the extent of my reason

wild

unregulated
the words weighed
on the scale of doubt
where charts eat numbers

and spit

a terrified faith

affection was cut
to new measure
and the heart bled love
on the hands of the unfaithful

your certainty was relative
but so was my devotion

a flight risk

you started looking for a wife
and so
i went looking for other men
because the love of the one i had
was grudgingly given

this quest drew up
the beat of the jungle
and leather car seats in the morning

body strapped for protection
stiff in its trappings
as the world lay outside

so strong and loud

and the hands slid
where there was no meaning

did you fuck that guy
yes
did you like it

no

they found me everywhere
kind strangers and predators alike
familiar and unfamiliar faces
all simply appeared
to and from places
in churches and train stations
uncalled for but eager

to catch

my fleetingly injured smile

being away from you
i forgot
how the consistency of love felt
every new body had that potential
so why were they not the ones
while i still had

a lot of heart

left to give

the Devil holds a magnet
to bend
the blasphemy of your thoughts
it can make things happen
it can swallow entire timelines
spitting you out like a fish-bone
your life
suddenly disremembered

fear gripped your hands
and two car crashes later
you started looking for a cure

i am not the disease

                    look at me

                    i am a city

i am a home well imagined
i am dizzy hours
on your parents' bed
i am lunch at sunset
and joy

                    as the deepest secret

that can concede your chosen burden

i am a pastel morning
too early to speak

rubbing into fountains and tiles
looking to discover
its own name

i am the secret
that your secrets keeps

now
bolt

thoughts betray me
racing after the time lost
halting muscle at my core
meanwhile
my mother dreams

again and again

of her thumb
injured so deeply
that it has turned black

she thinks her dreams are of the future
she frets over my footsteps
but little does she know
that dreams are always of the past

i cry

patching the fibres
of my messy heart
and this vision
comes to her again

elder brother's betrayal

Jonathan's complaint

Oslo, 2012-2015

there was a blood bond we shared
so i made my way to your house
to enter your peace

you are mine

                      mine to me[5]

you said
and my dreams ceased to matter
my eyes turned
to the bellies of women
walking with potential

             of skin

---

5   reference to the wolf pack in R. Kipling's *The Jungle Book*

and prayer

stretched to share
lust
transferred through airwaves

she buried herself in my resume
but lifted eyes full of love
and the rings were exchanged
by the hands that would never wear them

only then did i look at her

brother

i came to you in my hour of need
for you to believe in my lifeline
when i found it worthless
but you crossed out
the legitimacy of my doubts
and sent me on your way
before i had the chance
to find mine

my sadness has grown legs

and become

another person
living within me

i fed it her tears
and we mused
that we were not that young anymore

that i forgot
the tongue of my thoughts
that the old
would continue to get older

        leaning heavier
        on our choices

there is so much life
still unspent
bouncing off the walls within me

        until

losing hope for the day
i sink
into the thickening atmosphere

i spoke to you after bedtime

        darkness deepening my uncertainty
        and concealing your impatience

and the advice you gave me was
just get on with it

for the strength of the Pack is the wolf
and the strength of the wolf is the Pack[6]
and our questions grow into us
having no space to stretch

        so listen to my tongue
        harden

---

6   reference to the wolf pack in R. Kipling's *The Jungle Book*

a jealous year

Exeter, 2013-2017

I used to be hopeful

but now I am a woman betrayed

That year pretty girls with raven hair and confident shoulders accompanied me, reminding me of how invisible I was. The swoosh of their locks set tornadoes loose in my soul. I analysed the steady sparkle of life that gleamed in their lively brown eyes, letting it play on my mind in an agonising loop as I tried to understand how I could emulate the ease of their existence. If I wanted to be with you, I had to become one of them. Your parents' wish was a law unwritten - they only wanted a Malayali girl for your bride. And so, I watched the movements of these unattainable creatures, desiring to be them, desiring to forget myself in the certainty of their fate.

These wonderful women unknowingly had a bigger claim over you than your girl of many years. You could not introduce me as the one and so every dark-haired goddess I crossed paths with had the potential to take my place in a careless gesture that would cost a life. My life. The life, which was so far away from you, like a mirage, light and easy on the eyes, collecting into form on demand to keep your attention. So easy to turn away from, to switch it off as if it was only on TV.

You were a tame creature at heart, simple things brought you happiness, and a calm life with any of these girls would have made you content. Their smiles would have eased you into compliance and your family would have been proud.

Was this what you thought when years later you chose her? You were looking for simple things: a car, a job, a companion. A smiley round Indian girl, unaware of your depth. She would be drowned in it, lost in her own tears, confused how she had waded into the quicksand of your moods without even watching her step.

I always had the hardest time at the airports. In bigger airports, I was surrounded by Indian families, travelling in the bustle of children, grandparents, cousins, and in-laws. Multiple generations uprooted at once, guarding each other carefully for fear some would get lost from Tradition. The world is vast, but time is bigger. They always looked so effortlessly together, happy, and completely immune to the glares their confident loudness drew to them. On a good day, I soaked in their glee, my insecurities folded away for the time being. On a bad day, I drowned in their laughter.

You were jealous too. Your jealousy was strong and reaching. I belonged to you and so you had to be the provider of my happiness, the companion to my wanderings, the scholar of my thoughts. Your fingers curled to yourself when you thought of me having expressive conversations with strangers, laughing over a common incident with eyes flashing temptation. Our lives should have paused when we were apart but against our own wish they did not. We clawed desperately at their tails, trying to catch the news of the day, begging each other for the lie of having been there.

When you left after our first year, I asked you to collect stories for me. I was on a mission to get to know your home, to establish how the floorboards bend and bedsheets crinkle, how the sand grains move over the pavement like waves. By the grace of your narrative, I was the first to know about Meera. You told me your daily stories and I translated them for you. This married woman who shaped her eyes with kohl and wore skirts in your presence, walked with you to the bus stop every day, never touching, and yet I knew of her desire. Unhappiness in marriage was after all not in any way special, the vow that was placed on your lips did not create a union if all you did was swallow it meekly. Being a frustrated man, you allowed her to lead you into her husband's bed, all in my full attention, and teach you how love was made in the underworlds of arranged matrimony. I cried but I forgave you. She was the unhappiest woman I had ever known.

You could not understand my forgiveness, and neither could she. To you both it signified a love that shrivelled into apathy, while all I could see was the gravity doing its part: this ghost of once a happy woman, clad in laces on her marital bed, had more right to you than I did. In those few hours a week, she lived. Her husband, devoted and loving, never knew what it meant to have a lover like that.

But I lived too only when I got to see you. I told you that. You heard the words, but the meaning got lost in the empty vacuum of space between us.

All the pretty Indian girls led to a pretty Indian wife, adorned with her own trust and sense of righteousness. Her eyes had the same forward gleam of life that dared you to approach it. She could fight. She was direct. She wanted babies to place between you and herself at night. It was after all her right to ask for it.

But you had not settled. One day you screamed across the dinner table at your parents, asking them why they wouldn't just arrange the rest of your life for you. They had made all the decisions so far; it would simply be easier for all parties involved if they took over. They were surprised, they did not know what had brought this on. They thought you followed their lead keenly, your life stitched by your own hand.

They had decided for you… Were you not given a voice? Why did you allow it to be taken away? You should have gone wild but instead you sank your teeth into your own flesh and drew your own blood to punish yourself. Tamely, you tried to wish me away. Have a happy life, dear! But you could not. If I had a happy life, you would have incinerated yours to get at me.

Your wife kept quiet by your side but at night she wept. Divorce does not exist in your community and so there was nothing you could do now. Babies, babies would make love grow. Babies, over which you would also fight like they were a foreign territory: how to name them, baptise them, teach them, feed them, share them. You would get weary, and your tired complacency would be keenly mistaken for the patience of love.

I asked you to ceaselessly remind your family of your frustration. It would not change a thing, but they deserved the discomfort. The idea of me was uncomfortable to them so they got rid of the girl they did not care to know.

God is almighty but he too worships Tradition.

Their charity was selective. It was not meant for girls with pink apple cheeks and sun-kissed ponytails. Now may the absence of me steal their senses.

They took my heart slice by slice and pulled it out through my eyes when I lay in bed screaming. And so, I took away the sanity of their son. With him, I feasted on the blind taste of their Tradition. The kingfish curry had been protected by many generations, the recipe kept in the family and passed on to the next wife. You opened your wife's notes, wrote down the secrets and mailed them to me.

kingfish curry

little kingfish guards
guard little kingfish fish
they speak empty voices
of air bubble ancestors
grumbling at people
generations removed

carefully written
carelessly placed
by women
who felt safe lounging lazily

in their own homes

sealed by Tradition

unfairly taken
fairly given
by men who gave up voices

but kept

eyes and hands to build dreams with

dearly beloved
yet never missed
delicate notes were bottled

in suppressed kitchens

where pepper dusted footsteps linger

little kingfish guards
guard little kingfish fish
in the absence
of curry scented order

as i pulled it
from under their feet

bountiful mother

bountiful mother
the winner of the game you did not have to play

                  since you were groomed for it

your overflowing breasts
tempt the hands of your man
to receive them with grace

                  but you confer them

to your new-born instead

oh supple one

                  palms cupped

your man succumbs
to the ceaseless motion of your hips

                  aroused

by your walk to the kitchen

your plump skin
drips honey of assured contentment
and he gets trapped
on the naked floorboards

afternoon embraces
present themselves to you
begging hungrily
for your pregnant touch

these joys
you multiply

but peaceful morning glory
and his unyielding devotion
only ever come prepaid

looks of adoration
are bestowed upon you
by those less fortunate

immaculate
you face the altar
on Sundays

your role amongst your people
radiates elegantly
from your shape

that home of the nation

and draws praise
from the blood of others

you are fortunate enough

to see the jealousy
but not to need it
to feel the passion

        faintly
        from beyond
        a lustrous thing
        dimmed by the protection
        of the membrane of your skin

but to remain a goddess
worshipped
yet beyond our reach

slow days marked
by sleepy baby powder dust
sustain your trust in destiny
but it has been
a long time since
you doled
your last incarnate gifts

i prayed a little prayer
of fuck-you in the morning
to let my animus roam free
and so as if it was
ordained by God
society
and schedule
that evening you were fucked
to satiate my anger

        or his plea

the reluctant romantic

Abu Dhabi / Exeter, 2015-2017

Jonathan and Joana. It looked like fate, something meant to be: matching names, matching experiences, matching skin and two sets of happy families. Yet you were afraid to give it time. Arranged marriage is not supposed to have time. Time is for changing your mind. And so, you clenched your jaw and held your ground while I begged you not to go ahead with it.

The happiness we had shared weakened me. I gifted my dreams to you only to have them replayed back with another woman becoming the protagonist of my story. When you went to meet her for the second time, you kissed her secretly, weeks before you were supposed to. It was your docile rebellion at the arrangement that had brought you two together, and you liked that. You had your honeymoon in Maldives - another dream of mine you had refurbished to fit a new life. An invisible bystander, I watched squirming in pain, unable to peel my eyes off as I judged the authenticity of your love story. *Does it look good? Has it worked out? Is it real enough?* My jealousy confirmed in agony, but I tuned in for more, addictively looking for the cracks in the perfect picture.

When I broke up with you, you cut all connection, but you could not stop thinking of me moving on and loving other men. You crashed your car twice as your mind rushed forward to imagine the worst of me at every traffic light. You came back to talk to me only when you started looking for a wife. You felt safer in the world where love was structured and issued with a warranty. The first girl you tried to marry was in tune with her emotions. She called off the arrangement in a New Delhi hotel room. It was because of her that I got to see you again. But did you really see me then?

As if to tick it off, you finally told your parents that there was a fair-haired European girl you liked. You could say it because you had already given up. Just as you anticipated, they did not want to hear about me. It was easier to reject someone without knowing anything about them. Their faith in God did not stop them from deliberately hurting a stranger.

He shall live to run with the Pack and to hunt with the Pack.[7]

You let them do it. Secretly, without me knowing, you placed your hopes in an idea of a hollowed type of love which only stretched to the extent of your duty.

And then Joanna appeared and enabled you to arrange your happiness. You played a power couple at work and in church, your love was pronounced in pictures, you were a rational man and therefore your connection to your wife was strong and conscious. It looked like you had found yourself an ideal partner.

You contacted me because you were furious. At me for allowing you to go through with this, at yourself for doing it. You stoked your anger hoping to draw strength from it and

---

7   reference to the wolf pack in R. Kipling's *The Jungle Book*

cut yourself off from me. You selected memories to humiliate me and laid them bare in front of me like evidence of a crime: my incompetence, my failure, my childishness. Your happiness. I cut the call and your fury overflowed, stealing your being. I was not yours anymore and it terrified you.

In the end, it was the quiet acceptance of your discomfort that made you strong. You did the greatest romantic deed possible and allowed her to control your life according to her liking at the cost of your privacy and independence. Suffering had made you aware of your responsibility towards your speedily constructed family. My irrational force of love could not make you a stronger man, but your prearranged love did, and I bowed to that in painful admiration.

You contacted me again because you were love-starved. You wanted me to be the same as before, to narrate to you a fantasy, to send you a picture, to surround you with my admiration and make you forget. You felt I ruined your life and so I deserved the demands you were placing on me. But by injuring me, you had crippled my desire to worship you. We could not face each other anymore. At last, a bitter finality was setting in.

I cannot remember how I spent your first year in marriage. While you lazed in bed and savoured all the new joys of getting to know a new body, I worked 70-hour weeks, undressed myself in front of unfamiliar men to check whether they too declared me invisible, and travelled to 12 countries in 12 months. I was on a mission, a nomad with no present chasing hope which I had not yet been inspired to find. I crunched through songs to stifle quiet moments in fear that stillness would allow space for contemplation. On slow mornings, I found that tears produced new tears, and my hands clasped hysterically at my worn chest to stop them from spilling over.

But when I met people, I hung onto them like they were the hope itself. I made them laugh and surrounded them with my attention until their hearts warmed up to me. I looked into their eyes soaking in these sensations, like a chameleon wrapping myself around the atmosphere to remind my body how it feels to be a part of it, even if only by the comforting lie of mimicry. In this little island of somebody else's joy, my body would relax, and my heart would let go of its chains.

Strangers and friends alike did not understand my moods, but they could tell I was living with a mysterious passion driving me forward. I turned my pain inside out; even though I was drowning in it, I transformed it into a point of gravity. Others were pulled towards it to slip into its sudden depth.

There were moments when I smiled, and those moments were intensely vibrant.

You contacted me because I messaged you on every platform I could. With a sarcastic smile playing on your lips, you called me foxy. For the first time in months, you started to feel your control over me coming back. You no longer had to beg. And I was consistent too; I had asked you before you got married to let me at least keep a friend even if I was losing a lover. You never gave your word. I now found the strength to extract this promise from you.

I thought about death a lot, but I refused to seek it. When I got overwhelmed with my wish for oblivion, I would tell myself that a character killed off at the beginning of the story can never find out what happens next. The narrative does not stop for anybody. In my own story, I would be forgotten. And so, I got up every morning and made sure people relied on me in order to leave less and less time for the greedy agony to hoard. I even found a boy according to your recipe of arranged love, who shared my experience of pain, who was kind and thoughtful but imperfect enough to allow space for the guilty pleasure of your memory. Ultimately, I could not feel anything new: only the old feelings made sense, and it scared me.

When you would not talk to me, my sleep would be warped by nightmares. Being my mother's daughter, I understood the real cost of dreams and how they bubble up from under the conscious thoughts to tell uninhibited truths we are too worried to see. I dreamt that your wife was pregnant before you told me. I dreamt that you would meet me in secret before we even started talking again. I dreamt of your face hovering above mine before you revealed to me that you pictured me constantly. You were stubborn and ambitious, you asked questions like "what is the point of us?", but against your own reasoning, you never left. Was it my willpower that made you stay? I asked you not to forget me and you said you really tried to do the opposite of that.

You contacted me because I dreamt of you. I was screaming in my sleep, and you started from yours not knowing why. You felt the hunger permeate you like something material that fills you up instead of making you aware of an urgent scarcity. You wanted me to remain the miracle of your ordinary existence, so you grabbed your phone and reinstalled hope.

That's when I started narrating my pain to you. You were doubtful, yet after you had heard me, you never left. You could not understand how my love for you had survived; calmly, patiently it waited for the next time it would be allowed out of its cage to leave marks all over your body. I developed an addiction for dreaming up our future. But my dreams were made from the tapestries of our past where I lingered too often to be able to create anything new.

At night, when your wife looked into your eyes and asked soberly whether you had someone else, you said no. She did not know better; she could only rely on her senses. Her senses told her you could love her more. She did not know that your heart was not cheating on her as much as it was cheating on its own wishes. Cheating the systems of hope is how it knew to survive.

In this magical dreamscape of rippling shadows in the non-present time, we found each other by tracing our shapes in patient vigil. Who was to tell whether we were even there? This was where this story really began:

She held him by his soul. His dreams she kept safe from the world: tucked in her skirts, slid into the laces between her breasts. Dreams she nurtured, but worries were not given to her. They did not sink into the atmosphere; they could only be shared with the living. Stuck in another dimension, she spun the silver-webbed time between her fingertips. It moulded to her touch like a lonely forest spirit that longed to be held again. She was the weaver of hope, but she was living in darkness.

to the Mother

mary did you know
your son hurt a girl once

she was a lot like you
a bob

      a smile

            a little hopeful

a daughter
seven times removed

braided before bed
the morning stairwell spirit
alone until the first touch
whom you renounced
before meeting
the colour of her eyes

did you stop to think
whether she deserved it
or have you asked yourself since
where is she now

your son hurt a girl once
but it was once many times
in the eternity of her memory

from over the moon she dropped

                      to under the sunset

and the red shoes she wore that day
were fashioned from her own skin

they left an uncomfortable footfall

                    on marble

                    her pain slid down

the membrane of your ignorance
you paused
and as your hands returned to work
the disaster was contained

in perfect silence
chop chop chop

it was your recipe
that he burnt her tongue with
and stained her insides
with your hand-made judgement
but her screams
never shook your world

he hurt a girl once

you trained his heart for searching
you commended its restlessness
so he trapped her spirit
in the hotel shower
and watched her be reborn
warm and blind in trust
in time for reckoning

her sadness brought an axe
and broke her ribcage
declaring her brutally free

Mother

Father

Priest

the halo of your blessings
tore the cloth of her innocence
and she was unable to swim
against her own bloodline

as vows were exchanged
her shadow stood freshly hurt
at the end of the aisle

                                        almost not there
                                        in soft focus

in appachan nirav's ethereal shot
of the church framed
by pristine flower arrangements

and your anger felt righteous

                            then

but you averted your eyes
to spare her no thought

all thoughts ran away
to make space
for her meaning

eight times your son hurt a girl
and once

                            mary

you leaned
on the hand with the knife
to help him do it

you press play

Exeter, 2017-2018

sultry mistress rises at dawn,

declaring the fall for the day;

you watch me at work, undoing the distance

each time you press 'Play'.

You come to me timid, doubtful of the purity of your motivations. Is it guilt that traps your gaze? Your hunger is ever so subtle yet constant, it accumulates into crushing headaches. You lose your voice to it and your eyes dig into me feverishly, speaking of the trap you have laid for yourself. We both know you have been lusting after other bodies, but this moment in this rectangle of illuminated space is made bespoke and feels familiarly seductive to you.

I dance for you in this impossible dimension. First, it's against the backdrop of a little church in a narrow alley, prematurely culminating in a dead end, lined by fanning sari-clad women, their repetitive movement glimmering in the sun-warped shadows. Then, the Corniche after 6pm when the humidity lifts and reveals the stars. I move for you in my most precious memories. They are the everyday places you still visit with your wife._

I dance for her too. I want her to see your eyes as my casual grace melts their guard. I wish to catch her in the wilderness of art where I still hold the power to hurt her. Insecurity is the punch I throw well; it imposes foreign beliefs. Has she not learnt yet to take her dreams of romance out of hiding and smash them on the pavement for all to see? Just like you, she was asked to do that in order to prove her allegiance to her family. But I was there before her, meeting sunsets at the edge of the desert, at war with her people. And I am still here now. We live off each other's pain, her and I, wrestling for control over your time spent in our dimensions. She does it unknowingly while I target the soft pulp of her eyes.

If your marriage was rooted in true affection, it would not frustrate you. You go through notions of looking for solutions but still miss your freedoms. Under your skin, anger runs hot with a reflex to sting. I can neither fix it nor cause it. I am just a shadow, a symptom. Your desire for unfamiliar touch under the streetlights is what gives you nightmares, but you say it's normal. Normal for frustrated married men. In these words you hear the marginality of your own life.

And I am greedy and selfish too. I burst through time and space to present to you an image of a girl in a bubble, forever repeating herself on your phone screen. The image lives, replaying the geography of my body. Read it. You wanted proof of my love and so I recorded the hesitant curves that turned apprehensive after your marriage, the skin that shines anointed in defiance of my grief.

Hot Asian chicks are looking for older men. Hot Eastern European females are looking for experienced lovers. Click. Your girl is taking a bath and she is lonely. She undresses for a smart, capable guy. He watches with a twinkle in his eye: from the privacy of his car, in the confines of his bathroom, at night when his house is asleep. You press 'Play' and release yourself into a fantasy. There is little made up in it. Little but the proximity of these bodies.

I narrate myself to you at the moment when the concentration of life in your body fights for its way out and finally overwhelms you, offering yourself to me, dying a small death of relief at my feet. Desire is a weapon in the battleground for control, surrender cracks like a whip but its bite fills you with a sudden wave of relief.

She wants to come in sometimes, she wonders what you do, she forbids you to touch yourself and you hurriedly deposit your desire into the cooling tiles. She knows you are unhappy – you shouted it across the table once. But she only wants her right by law – to try and be your muse. She cried that night as the knowledge sank into her; she was living in somebody else's marriage.

It is not my body; it is my presence trapped that heats your blood. In this portable, pocketable form I cannot be removed from you. Only you can choose to clear out your secrets. Until then, I will continue to provide. I am your Miss Nils Karlsson[8] and I sleep in an empty box of matches on a pinch of cotton fluff. It is this careless arrangement that our delusions are made of.

I was never a girl of striking features, but I have filmed myself for so long that I have become photogenic. I direct these lustful narratives, coming up with endless settings from my dim cramped room, taking pleasure in my own liquid shape on the screen. Your insatiable hunger for more is the

---

8   Nils Karlsson is a character in one of Astrid Lindgren's stories - Nils Karlsson Pyssling. It is about a lonely boy, named Bertil, who finds a little boy living in the mouse cave in the wall and takes care of him. Part of the story involves using everyday items to help furnish Nils's little apartment, such as a match box for the bed and cotton for the blanket.

power that moves my hand, and like a mother bird feeding her baby chic I go hunting for another story. And tonight, just like any other night, I am here, moving to the drums of your lusting heart, in the smoke of our dreams.

delivered

sir oh good sir
stop for a moment
taste our cut of the day
you do not have to pay
or even speak of it

sir oh kind sir
come hither
your meal will get cold
sit and unfold

                while we serve you
                your dream

finely sliced
graciously delivered
limited availability
your discounted Russian

                all legs
                fresh
                from LT

i will find you

Exeter, 2015-2018

Some days you hide from me. You know you belong to me, and you get consumed by guilt when you stray with another woman. You think that distance can help you. I am the spirit that follows you through the shadows on your wallpaper, slicing through your excuses and gripping onto your trembling core. My voice beheads your remorse as you think back to the times spent with me and find them faultless. Love in your life has become a duty, and so you find yourself in a happy family, but you are not happy in it.

You cannot hide from me, boy. I know exactly what you are thinking, and it scares you. It scares you even more that I know what I want and hold it with the grip of the one who holds her destiny. You used to believe that I did not understand you. I was only being cautious. Now, years after our last meeting, I close my eyes and still read you like you are within my skin. Your thoughts find home in my pulse, they defy your wishes and turn to me to surrender themselves. I do not need to call you. As soon as you sense me, you come to me, helpless, guiltily hovering around the edges, patiently waiting to be called in.

Why would you think this time is any different?

You tried to make love to your wife in defiance of how you felt, and you could not satisfy yourself. You, so full of unapplied desire that your manhood overflows when you see my careless skin. You, who has tasted passion, but got a girl who will not spread her legs wider than proven to be the standard requirement to conceive. You thought that a couple of discussions over coffee were enough to prepare you both for navigating life in the clumsy mud of each other's hurt and discomfort. Giving yourself time would have seemed almost like finding reasons not to do it.

Believing that you could not achieve your dreams, you set yourself a mediocre standard. You even dared to say that you wished I found a nicer guy than you. But you never wished for my happiness, you said it only to justify your own misery: look, I was not right for her; look, she is doing great without me; look, I have made the right choice. You cannot outplay me, boy. I have reached into myself in sorrow and pulled out my hand dripping with cooling messy thoughts only to find that I have no fear. Instead, I discovered vision that cuts through matter. When I close my eyes, I see myself standing at the core of my existence. I was once a beautiful, sad butterfly. You tried to kill me, and I scarred my own wings to make them tougher. I am hovering on the flipside of your world just to prove you wrong; I am stronger than the death you sentenced me to.

When you told me you would be getting married to another, I told you that I would haunt you. You were shocked. You believed I was nice! We are made from the same cloth – two people, holding awful selfish love – and you will never be able to free your mind from the desire that I arouse in you. I prophesy the truth onto your fear. My words resonate in you and your discomfort amplifies them. And if one day you will feel like running away, I will hunt you down. Your promises were reserved for people who held fear over your head. So, I said to you: pain has sharpened my vision. Be afraid. Without arrows or spears, my words will lure you out of hiding and hurt you... to heal you.

I am the woman who waltzes around her room, splashing pain on the white walls without a drop of mercy on her place of rest. A woman who whispers to the wind, drawing blood from her memories. A woman who conjures songs of your grandmother's youth from the vibrations in space. Her stories are my stories now, to hear your history ring with life you will need to come to me. Do you dare doubt me?

My want for you will not allow me to enjoy anyone else. This has turned me into a huntress. You did not believe we were meant to be, so I made us be exactly that. We are meant now because I mean it. You are afraid your wife will find out, will see through your half-truths. She has caught you breaking promises before, she has distributed guilt. Do not worry, honey. She has obtained you by following instructions. It is I who has learnt patience from stalking prey. It is I who roams into the uninhabitable wilderness and finds herself wilder than anything in it. It is I who holds the sinews of your tender pulsing heart.

you wouldn't take
me before God, so
I went to the
Devil's side

Mumbai, 2018

i cannot write about India while

i am there

i can only fit it into the confines

of my memory

after the time moves it away from me

and that in itself is a kind of deception

a narrative in the fog of my love

for what it means

but never for what it is[9]

thin light shrouds the edge of the jungle

and cuts the boatman's silhouette

into horizontal lines

but it is my contrasting loneliness

that gives me headaches

i saw a lot before i saw you

but India came into focus only then

love

you crash my every fantasy

to outshine it into misery

you

the maker of dreams

how do i dare to see myself fulfilled

how can i imagine me a future

with that

which i have not known

i met an old lover at the crossroads again

where nothing was certain

---

9   inspired by the idea of the other in Edward Said's *Orientalism* and Joseph Conrad's *Heart of Darkness*

i want you to come to life for me
i want you to feel like home to me
just for one night
i long to be
at peace

uncles flying on their motorcycles
their lungis flapping about
their makeshift shrines rattling in the speed
their smiles staying behind to play
with my expectations

                              silly girl

we have no interest in your charm
we have wives and we have children
your presence does not alleviate our hunger
your matchstick legs
will carry you to the next city
but your heart will shiver and break
unless you too find
the pressure point for your need

                              to see

how headlights tear the dust
ahead of you before sunrise

i came to see the watchmaker
he wound your watch to my heartbeat
and the sun burnt my wound shut
revealing a fresh speck of innocence
but the watchmaker was watching time
sand grains pouring over short-lived stories

and his regrets made him love the seconds longer
longer than he loved his days

my lost lover

it is as if i sleepwalked my way to you
i smelled the dusty air in my dreams
hours before my plane touched the ground
the damp heat cocooned me into its womb
where i walked in lazy comfort

with families
and stray dogs

who did not notice me

and the waves were beating the shore
and the sun burnt the edges
and the dusk was dreamy
and the guard was a romantic shape in the distance
while the wife kissed her husband
as a seagull dived across the picture
and their sweetness melted
into the dying light

Mumbai

you were my city of dreams

we walked hand in hand
the potholes were happy
the tinted tea was happy

and the breakfast lady
smiled a lot

the pool was our looking glass
and strangers admired our brazen charm
of being together
of you touching my woven swimsuit waist
of loving the sun-kissed parts of me

                     underwater

reflecting off your aviators

the guard smiled at us
each time he did his rounds

                  the faithful sentinel

he saluted

                a myth
                our hope
                his miracle

                Mumbai

we were your dream

you did not wear your ring
but i wore mine
the ring with roots and branches

                twisted

like salty wood
growing into my sinews
my independence
growing into me

deeper each time
you answered a call
from your wife

          guilty

you paced the lobby
whispering care
dispensing daily love
while i stayed outside

          in the sun

protected by the walls
not hearing

          but hearing everything

not seen
but rocking the balance of things

          observing

the adoration you show her
and the picture
with laughing jawlines

and despite all your care
i cannot unsee that
i smash over it again and again
like a wave that cannot help its course

          i will grow out my faith
          just like i grow out my hair
          from the steady quiet roots
          of my heart

in the hotel world
of honeymoons and conferences
we were the lucky dreamers
i stood naked at the window
up high while you slept
palm tree shadows
falling over my mood
majestic structures hijacked
by the glimmer of the sea

a black rubbish bag
hot and reckless
moved in mindless circles

           where nobody would ever come
           to look for it

in the lazy breeze
that inert pawn of fate
unconcerned with time

sometimes
i feel a thousand years old
and once i feel it

           i look it

fighting against my sober self
to remain young and careless
for you
and bring you abundant riches

           of pleasure

Mumbai

in you we slept dreamlessly

but what if i stay
stay stay stay said the echo
stay stay stay said the dream
as another lonely soul
climbed the heat drops
and plugged their hope
in the night

stay stay stay said the city
stay stay stay your heart cried
who found its illusion in me
for I am your mistress now
but you would never call me that

***

Sun was a fireball, rising majestically from the agony of the dusty city, surrounded by purples and oranges, imprinting itself on a bruised sky. Yet another birth - mine, into the determination of keeping love in iron armour, indestructible and unfeeling, safe and measured, for an affair always starts from a position of power. But the armour is heavy, it presses uncomfortably into the untrained skin; a mistress can let the love run wild only a few days a year but for the rest of the time she must tow it as a burden.

I headed into the airport building but left my eyes behind, hurt by the spectacle of the ever-changing time. Restless babies at the departure hall screamed at the daylight, reminded of their own coming.

Is there a way to make all love matter on the same plain without it being opposed to each other? What happened to me, I brought upon myself. But regardless of the circumstance, all love is born innocent and hopeful. It waits on us, but we deny it its duty, yet we cry after it when it is not there anymore. We section it and redistribute it according to our whim. We never let it be as it is. But our own blood we feel for. We ache when our blood is sacrificed. Love that mixes with blood is the type of love that remains. Being deeper than emotion, it is carnally selfish.

apple sundays

the apple i bit into
smelled like the sex we had
one sunday afternoon
laced by flower-patterned shadows
my knees spread wide in trust
to receive grass whispers
scattered by low winds

you pulled down my white socks
skin throbbing with expectation
tongue out
for this season of pollination

i took a feather to write
my fruitful incantations
on your generous pulse
bursting with longing
but the ink rose over my palms
drowning the tense sheets

we lay in it

our bodies spilling over
euphoria rising
and chests falling
our lust settling in
to stay and become
resurrected in images

i have reached out to you
my fellow whisperer
beyond the time given to us
and they will call me a sinner

                    for it

after the
apocalypse

London, 2020

loud chaos of birds
flavours her shower with needles

                        of spring

sun too sharp and too early
sliding on the wet floor
and into the kitchen

coffee more placid than usual
waits patiently for the spoon
to part the reeds and launch
the steam into the light
expelling the slumber

she lays idle on the bed
hair rushing down
skin new and open to music
soothed by leafy shadows
lit by sparks of dust
spinning above
quickening
as they catch fire

                    she lays idly

filling her moments brim-full
as one does after the apocalypse
when days are as slow as solitude

little soldier dear

little soldier dear
at night your house asleep
you give in to your fears
hide love you cannot keep

sprinkled by the moon
your floorboards come aglow
loss haunts the silver spoons
loss makes your feet go slow

your ancient battles lost
have robbed you of your spear
but truly at what cost
little soldier dear

your kitchen mistress gone
where heartaches lie to rest
she dropped a single tear
to put love to the test

you bent to pick it up
and carry it to bed
it dropped into your eye
you followed where it led

futures

the one where I try on
the futures I might have had

the new city

Dubai, …

revenge was driving me
and so
i revved the engine to race
into the tall city
with buildings towering over
like glass shards
reflecting the sun
off their sharp edges

there
each taxi driver
wanted me
to be happy

nice boys
groomed boys
good degree boys
with flat smiles
all congregated
in 2D
on the sides of buses
red and ready
cheering me on
charging into the heart
of the big city

miss
pick me miss
why such a pretty girl alone
settle down
get it out of the way
plenty of nice boys around
falling at your feet
at the finish line
they will give you
nice babies

marriage

        marriage

                marriage

there was no time left
but everyone who raced
was allowed to forget this
for they would reach
the finish line
a winner anyway

a winner

holding trophies of abundant teas
Ferrari parks on weekends
and naughty children
hugging strong hips of the woman
whose sense of purpose
once sprouted in her bone marrow
to give her fate a nudge

loneliness did not exist in this world
and the little voices
that cried otherwise
struggled to break free
from their parents' timeline
and perished away
from the unwillingness
to hear them

your desires clung to you
like hot tire marks
leaving sores all over your memory
and i kept getting lost
in a dream with a little boy
that our mothers held tenderly to their chests

while it echoed from the clock towers
that i was running out of time
to be beautiful

and although i raced to you
electric with intent
urged by the maddening sting

                         of betrayal

i knew
i would be a hypocrite
to say that i did not understand
why you gave yourself no time
and gave your parents
what they wanted

my angelic sister

Kerala, …

Angel, you stand protected by the lines of bodies of so many who did not want you to fall like a pawn, victim to the strikes of my imagination. He instinctively knows that he must guard you from me even though I mean no harm. For you are not a common figure, skin shining like dark wood, you are the Queen in this story. Meanwhile, magic runs in my blood, its current still wild with the same unbridled energy that powers volcanoes, and the possibility of it spilling out of its tracks makes my eyes shine with dark flame.

Yes, Joana, I have been made into your nemesis.

I reach through the membrane of time to understand you. It fights the pressure of my touch and snaps back, leaving your slender form shrouded in mystery. Elusive, your image blurs in my thoughts like a chalk shape on the pavement to mark a crime scene. But Angel, what is this crime I stand accused of? You are of the same blood, you and I, and if I ever spill yours, my own veins will run dry. All I seek is to know the taste of your choices. It would be blasphemy for me to make it all up.

You say, shaking with righteous anger, that I can never be like you, my unfallen sister. A Queen cannot assume her role without being chosen. And so, you hate me for you see me in your reflection.

Your first love betrayed you too. He went to your best friend and made her undress before daylight, meeting sunrise without shame next to blinded windows. This played on your mind in wonderful detail, slashing the life in your soul.

Us women know how anger makes us work against ourselves. He knew your domestic heart and trusted its loyalty, but he found himself dethroned as you crowned your newly found husband. He forgot that you too felt the pressure point to please your mother with your life. He forgot that your womanhood gave you choices.

Now your skin joins mine to slither away from the wound, made vulnerable by deception. You, so beautiful and pure, in no way deserving of this, and me, who dived into chaos headfirst, like a storm white with anger. Now both of us must lay still, growing out new resilience.

So, tell me, my angelic sister, how did you guard your heart to go through all this without breaking?

Your silence permeates my thoughts.

I do not hold the right to know.

to the Wife

Kerala, …

i am not a threat to you

he picked you
injured by kisses shared
without your permission
by your own pride
breaking heart's choices
by pleading whispers

i am leaving you
but do not give yourself to her

you walked backwards
to find your past again
unwillingly left
for the best friend to care for
your dreams to her bowing
vanilla stained lips liberated
and your lover's hand
now bravely in hers

your friendship has become
your greatest tragedy
that cut into your choices
and you now know
if love was once taken away
it will never be returned

the world went dark
as you found yourself
painfully interchangeable

you have rebuilt your life
according to the past you knew
so your present hurts you the same
and i am not a threat to you
but you look for my thorns

under your skin

you chose him
because you no longer wanted

to be able to see

because you longed to wish
your eyes away on children
because you knew
it took effort to forget
but nothing ever goes away
so the pain made you

oddly kind
dangerously indifferent

you watch him wearily now
finding only a nameless part of him
in your careful ecstasy

with him you chose me too

i am here
only when your heart knows of it

he went for a walk in the old jungle
by your family home in Kerala
while you were distracted
caressing your baby

soft and warm
all yours
happiness before reason

he came back
a subtle stranger

were there mistakes

you had not learnt from yet

to have your tragedy repeated

you ask yourself

as you hug your knees

yet again in darkness

the one with the billboards

Abu Dhabi, …

I make small kindness my daily pleasure
I reach out in conversation
so brittle
so sought after
in this lonely city

where everyone is grappling

with their own eternal homelessness

I was the artistic type. With round glasses, fly-away hair, delicate figure, and spurts of creativity that blotched my fingers with ink. It was my war paint and so you were always worried that I would go to battle and release a story into the world: to be judged, loved, and lived by. A story that called you by your name.

Dazed with pain, desensitised to time, I sat down and cried on paper, cutting out your traces from my memory with a spear-tipped pen. It was not pretty at first. Thoughts swelled with hope, thundering with flashes of hurt that were steady enough to let me live but stole my breath when no one was watching. Loneliness poisoned my sheets and pillow-muffled despair clattered in the infinite space within my lungs. The world walked by indifferently, but I knew you could hear it. And so, I wrote more, but this time with tender care for the words that would keep you close to me. Writing became the mast to cut through the exhausting mental fog wrapping my mornings, my way of understanding my place in this world, in your life.

One only understands the things that one tames[10].

If I knew anything about the world, it was that there was always space for another tragic love story. That was how this story was born.

The story took off, gaining the life of its own outside of me. I released the ghost at the core of my pain, and I could no longer bottle it. It bolted forward, leaving the scent of rain and the memory of footsteps on warm concrete. Printed and bound, it travelled from lips to lips, hugged by carefully grown women and picked apart by entitled voices: *he is toxic to her, why won't she move on... impressing on young minds... responsibility to her readers...*

---

10   from Antoine de Saint Exupery's *The Little Prince*

glorifying promiscuity... unfeminist expression...

I was pulled after it. Suddenly, I had to go to readings and events, I answered questions and wore backless gowns on demanding stages, long enough to cover my uncertain steps but revealing enough of my flirtatious skin to make me seem confident. You saw me on television once and felt a sudden sting of dread – the story was coming for you.

Then a play was born. Unexpectedly, you found yourself on the billboards of your city with me by your side, two ghosts on a journey to nowhere. I sent you the book, but you were too afraid to open it. That made no difference – it had spread its pages for all to see. How big a reach could my words have? Sold under the fiction label, they were read like a diary of a nefarious woman. This woman had a face that made an occasional appearance in the gossip columns of weekend papers. She was smuggled into the ventilated living rooms of righteous aunts and their love starved daughters. Pressed to guilty bosoms, her face heeded no borders.

When your Liverpool cousin noticed the inscription, your family retreated inwards to reflect on what business your name had sliding in between the pages of this promiscuous prose. Their eyes turned to you, silently persisting on explanation, drilling deeper to see what you had dared to keep away. Nobody tried to ask outright, they asserted to themselves that they knew the truth because they knew you, one of them therefore just like them: singularly content, certain of his purpose. It was only a matter of time before a mother or a wife, weakened by heartache, would sound their demands for an explanation. Their own sacrifices in the name of their love for you did not let them rest until they had what they thought they were owed: your entire, undivided self.

Heartache followed you like a river. You would not be able to trick it out of its course, to evade it or shake it off. These waters would not dry on your back. They would mark you. They would follow you on the news, on the street, commuting in the glances of strangers, riding the questions of journalists, trailing you in billboards and leading your job interviews. It would settle on your furniture like dust, suffocating your evenings.

***

She did not know what was true. Having been betrayed before, she knew that if she put trust in your words, she would only be numbing her worry. Trust was not to be parted with carelessly. But she also knew that the truth was too diverse to be captured. There was always a side, a narrative, a seemingly inconsequential detail she would not have the insight to consider. There, in the open, bold in its stance yet quietly waiting to be noticed, it would reason her into empathy. Was she ready to devilify the villain? Past was gone, its stories could not be put under test again and would have to be laid to rest eventually.

She called me one evening and simply said:

"Tell me – what is true in this story? You wrote my life away without permission and now I cannot unpick this narrative."

"What does your heart tell you?" I asked, in absence of simple answers.

"It tells me that the loudest will always have the truth, but they will also fail to capture it. They will not be able to stop rummaging through their own words, anxiously trying again and again to be faithful to it."

Love was complicated. It reached past pockets of grief and into forbidden depths. We could only outlive things we accepted.

***

You grew to fear me in admiration. You hated how far my words have reached. They clutched you like a marionette and exposed you to scandalised whispers. *Did he really do a blonde? And after marriage? No way!* They stared, staying away from you, respectful of your power to spark condemnable envy.

Did you betray me? Or is it all fiction? She reached for answers without words, searching her depth and your helpless silence.

She exposed her moral degradation. What a slut! Shame, giving a bad name to her family and her country. Such a white girl thing to do, careless and immoral, all of them. I listened to the hate thinking that every painful comment also meant that the story was heard. They hated its liberty to be disgraceful, they wanted to remind themselves of why it was wrong, and so they read it again and again.

Immigration checkpoints became the stalls of judgement. Will they recognise me? Do they care? What do I mean to a country that censors literature? How many words will I be allowed to carry over to the other side? How much of my voice will be allowed to leave? I smiled every time thinking about my name – uncommon, a real tongue twister. I had nowhere to hide.

You came to one of my readings. She was not with you, but I knew that you got her permission – you brought your little girl. We walked along the Corniche, passed by runners and cyclists, under the date trees dropping fruit. I was never allowed to see your girl before. I had lived with the expectation of her, with fears of rejection, frustration over her otherness and love for her familiarity. She was mine more than I knew and unable to ever articulate it I hugged her to let her know that. Your little girl had a space of her own in our big imaginary universe and one day she will grow to recognise us by the dust we shake off at the door upon entering home.

***

I read from the Song of Solomon at your church. It was a community reading but I was assigned that part. In their eyes, I could no longer be shy; I have done unspeakable things, but I stood in front of them, whole, my back straight, meeting the eyes of those forgetful enough to stare. I read the tender, supple words well, in defiance of their expectation of my

115

shame, revealing to an embarrassed crowd the sweet spot of vulnerability. It dissolved into a shared sense of longing:

Let him kiss me with the kisses of his mouth—
for your love is more delightful than wine.[11]

And they listened, eyes wide, commanded by the words spoken by someone they knew had been loved and loved back in all its tumultuous forms. You placed your hand around your wife and reclined in your chair, feeling content having the two sides of your story united - something you had never felt was possible. She looked up at you, surprised. This was different. She leaned into your chest, finally finding there a piece of her home.

That evening I came over for dinner. She invited me out of curiosity for her sudden wish to know me. To understand why I had written the words I did, why I pleaded guilty to these words with the openness of a fanatic. She listened to my story again, narrated to her exclusively. The one from my heart to a woman who was also once wounded past recognition of her own path, swollen with emotion so big that it paralysed her. She thought how wonderful life was, with chaos that created parallels, pulling strangers together carelessly, like the seeds that settle wherever the wind scatters them. By opening her home and heart, she gained the most unlikely ally. Everything has a place and a reason. Love that passed its expiry date did not start to smell, it sprouted - painfully, insistently - and bloomed into something else. The universe was not wasteful.

---

11   The Bible, New International Version, Song of Songs 1:1-3

the making of a monster

One Thousand and One Nights retelling

i am afraid to disappear

                                        you said

to die
and truly die
recede from word
and memory

and time
and stories tell me that
to be remembered
i must trust
my desperate unconquerable darkness
to bind the ears of others
by will alone
and make
the tender bones pile up
to form a monster

stringing these words together
i slip to dress
an act of murder into sacrifice
and those that hear forget
what is the weight of story in my flesh
how it reanimates the flesh of others
with hungry wanderlust

and it is not the truth that matters
when stories are the means
to cheat the game of hours
by dressing cruel fates
with a coquettish touch
for the pleasure of the beholder

the wet grass smells like eagerness
and while i live

the monster lives

to tell a story for my life
means knowing
that people sometimes edge
terribly close to my dreams
and as i grow defensive
i repeatedly commit fallacies
against myself

and my language has no words
to contain the apology
or the depth

                              of this loneliness

to tell a story for my life
means approaching every morning

                         knowing

that my idea of happiness
as young as innocence
as short as fairy tales
will always end in marriage
to this constructed man
arisen from the bones
of my aging dreams

he comes
perpetually on a cusp

                         of bloodshed
                         or of lust

as the day breaks
i sigh with gratitude
for love saves lives
and stories have consistently told me
that monsters could
one day become
my greatest love affair
or darkest sacrifice

the one with the
violence

Abu Dhabi, …

He grants peace to your borders[12]

I lived my life struggling for joys, taken from another. I pulled you to me, but you would come with guilt and the guilt would remain in my presence long after you left, sprawled and lazy. I would call you over and

---

12   The Bible, New International Version, Psalm 147:14

with you would come the emptiness where the pain of your wife would one day rest. She did not know she had it yet.

Knowing that, my heart leaked and the time I had with you I spent checking my warped borders, wondering how much longer they would hold. When I lay with you, the passing days did not mark the quantity spent together but instead counted the time that was running out. It was always less than a moment before.

My heart was a little bullfinch trembling in the snow, frantically catching the seeds while the careless hand would spare them. Would they be enough to satisfy my present hunger? Would they be enough to help me withstand the future days of want? My future was to be made of the things I once had and then lost.

I was not allowed to re-enter your world any other way – the condition of your wife – and so I stayed a mystical woman who forced the time to roll backwards. I tumbled through the clumps of darkness into delirious dreams, imagining my own power to change fate. You would knock on my door and my kneecaps would buckle; the spark of my will would hiss into smoke. The darkness always had the last word.

But the heart is a muscle, it can grow weary.

It was a Friday morning, marked by sun-streaked pastels of sand and blue of the desert city. It was the day you went to church. I could not go, for I knew I had sinned.

I picked up a cricket bat and walked across the road in the uneven shadows of residential buildings. Their pointed windows showed no faces, their big white cars bejewelled dusty sidewalks. On a white street in a white world on a white morning, my anger made the shadows sink deeper into themselves.

You never took me to your place, but I knew where it was. Too many times I had dreamt of going there, staying there observing how a life lived in the presence of others felt like. Ah, the redeeming boldness of being seen! I was invisible to them, I lingered on the edges, a scared memento from the past. They never saw me there; they won't see me leave either.

They will feel it instead.

I followed my vision, and I ended up at your entrance, unlocked. There was a tight community in these buildings, nobody invested in security. There were always eyes to watch you fall.

I pushed through the heavy mahogany door and into the silence of an empty apartment. Surprised at how easy it was to come to this point, I stopped, taking a moment to immerse myself into the smells of another's existence. By breathing in, I have dived into their habits. They left fingerprints all over the place like it was a crime scene. The morning rush, the laundry cycle, the shower dew. With my finger, I traced the glasses in the cupboard, left handprints on a tiled wall. I peered into the sink, swabbed my finger across a washed-out pickle stain on a breakfast plate. I jumped on the brown sofa and kicked a salad green armchair. It fell sideways with a dull thud like it did not mind. It did not fit there anyway.

I headed to the bedroom and sat on the bed, looking up. Plain empty whiteness that could do with a new coat of paint. Could this sustain your desire? I lay down trying to extract the memories from the mattress, but it did not tell me much. It was a functional piece: children climbed over it at play, parents fell onto it in exhaustion, sometimes even forgetting to undress.

I started with your TV, smashing it so hard that the stand also cracked in two. It projected your dreams and so it deserved to crumble. We watched it naked once, but that was in another world, cradled by a different set of walls. I worked my way meticulously through the items in your apartment, crushing the cups and decapitating the chairs. I smashed mirrors and pulled cupboard doors off their hinges. I tore curtains by swinging on them like they were vines in a hostile jungle I came to conquer. I ran to the door draped like an emperor of a devastated city, surrounded by goose feathers sadly floating on the edges of my rage.

I ruled your kingdom.

You found me ankle-deep in the rubble. A little girl emerged from behind the broken chairs, clutching her giraffe toy by the neck, biting her tears back in silent terror. She ran to you and hid behind your leg. Overcome by the heat of destruction, I did not realise that I had an audience. Shocked, she peeked out from behind her shield and observed everything she desired to do but was never brave enough to try. I turned her home into a playground, into things that fell and lost shape, consequently becoming something new and yet to be named.

As you pulled me out by the hair past a handful of nosy neighbours hovering outside, I professed:

"Touch the shards, feel their edges. Can you see my pain now? Is it tangible enough to be considered? I hope this reaches the core of your being and spreads in all areas of your pathetic life. Fuck you and your fucking paper existence."

It was a spectacle to behold while it lasted. The neighbours slowly shuffled away as you burned with shame, watching your home being attacked from within.

becoming

Abu Dhabi, …

violent sunshine
cuts through the dazed mist
pulling the water up screaming

we move
time dragging behind
chopped by automatic doors
like a painting of sharp colour

a birth

or an assault at sunrise

dew will not fall here again
so step carefully
between the blades of your existence

tilted corner shadows
crash on the burning pavement
breaking the resistance
parched cracks
divide the glass
of the nearest office building

white is hysterical here
it hurts in self-defence
while the grass erodes
cringing away from your touch

as the morning rises
light sinks
with heat rolling off the tiles

there will be no barefoot joys
nor the cooling relief of rain
your tears will roll the dust
and fold it for simpler times
each morning will slap you
for it knows what's within you
untouched

unshared
invalidated

you will stand there all the same

scarring

the vision feels heavy
but it is not a tragedy
for tragedy is always loud here

broken senses give in
as i hatch like an egg

my dreams

rolling under someone else's bed

i gasp for joy
until i am
forgotten

the one with
another man

Abu Dhabi, ...

The man was not invited but he came anyway.

I did not encourage him, but he stuck around, suggesting books through the cracks in the library shelves, carrying my picnic basket on the weekends, laying the sheet on the beach for us to sit on. In my indifferent calm, he could share my presence without interrupting my thoughts. I laughed with him because he was kind to me. We shared a juice cocktail at the beach bar after a swim: one glass, two straws. We shared advice on domestic matters and a toolbox for quick fixes. We shared more and more time. I did not have a past, he did not have a family, we were not curious, but we learnt about the present together.

He did not have a name until he made me hear it.

I told you that I was going on a date, and you paused. You were still a weekend guest in my nomadic apartment, always counting time on your watch and looking over your shoulder. It irritated me that although you were worried you would lose me, you did not attempt to turn me into a genuine person - a friend. Rather, you preferred to see me as a forest fairy from a faraway land, there, yet magically out of reach, bottled in a glass city – a fantasy nobody else would look hard enough into your eyes to catch, and so your guilt could not be put on trial.

But one day others will look at me and see that I am of flesh and blood too. I had edged dangerously close to stepping into the real world and becoming real to somebody else. Suddenly, you started to feel exposed.

A date was... allowed. I deserved to find a nice man, my countryman whom I could rely on and be understood. You always wanted me to move on eventually so that you could too. But why did this thought feel so hollow now? You messaged me every moment you had to ensure I was still there but there were silent spaces wedged into our conversations now. They belonged to another man.

When his presence gained weight and started to fasten around me like a mouth guard, I told this man:

"I do not want to be a silly white girl, placed in a different world but still attempting to live by the rules which cannot work here. I do not want to seem to these people like I do not know the system just because you do not treat me as you would a woman from your community, offering me the same kind of respect. I do not want to hang around until you are married off to someone you almost like. I will not be your rebound lover that can never become your equal just because you will not allow yourself that freedom. I want to be real to you, not a fantasy or an opportunity, but a real person you want to be seen with."

Respectful of the intensity in my words, oblivious to the source of their inspiration, he listened to me. More importantly, he looked at me like he heard me.

He was not a fellow countryman you wished for me. You realised this when to meet his parents I dressed myself in the luxurious kameez you once gave me. You grew frantic, swaying between wild thoughts of my cosy evenings to assurance that I will be rejected. Too white, too Northern, too lean, I was simply the wrong kind of compromise.

He was divorced. He walked over rules, making them bend and shape to catch up with his stride. His mom invited me in, and his dad cracked jokes about Soviets over a glass of bourbon. He held my hand at the dinner table and kissed it as his brother was giving thanks. Everybody saw it and nobody flinched.

He proposed to me with a piece of string, wrapping it around my ring finger. He did it overwhelmed by the moment and thought to himself that good moments were rare - it was more important to catch them than to appear prepared. The ring he could get me later.

You tried to laugh at this. Was he a poet? An academic? Unemployed? Romance cannot take care of your future. Doctors, engineers, scientists can. You thought, relieved, that I met a rare kind of man, and you will not have to try and explain his life choices to yourself.

He was a web developer with a heart and a will to follow it. Romantic curls ran through his salt and pepper hair, matched with attentive eyes, mellow like liquid chocolate. Rooms stood to attention when he entered, ready to deserve the trust placed in him, but he also read beautifully slow literature on weekends and his strong hands felt light on my waist in careful consideration.

Your hope to paint him as less than yourself sank.

I told you after it happened. I was afraid I would change my mind if I saw your face before I put on a ring to mark my new allegiance. A thought crept over me, sweeping me into a moment of darkness: you could never touch me now.

"I hate you for being able to do this. Don't know how you manage to get what you want every time. Whatever you want you get! I hate you. I hate you. Did you fuck him in his family home too? I can never look at you again."

You shook in helpless anger, seeing my choices in direct parallel to your own. And yet, deep down you wanted him to succeed, to get to live what was once possible for you, but you also wanted him out of the way for the same reason.

You grew heavy with time, and I grew heavy with happiness. It showed. I wore it like a dagger, and you ached every time you ran into me. You saw the impact of another man on the shape of my hips, the fullness of my cheeks, the feel of my skin, and you could not escape the knowledge that someone else had made a mark on my life: flesh-deep, woven into habits.

You hid from me as much as you could, your body shrinking in daylight. It made space for mine, which expanded, magnetising glances of strangers until there was no more denying – I was with child.

Nobody told you this. You met me one evening and the ghostly look in your eyes made me unfold my arms, previously locked in self-defence. I was wedged like a door stopper between my past and my future, both of which were real to me. There was weight in our story which I had to carry around, enduring the consistent aching that came with it, but I also loved my husband. I loved him even more for the various ways he showed me daily that he was not you, that he was stronger than you, that he was… just like I would have wanted you to be.

I slapped you and we screamed at each other like two hyenas, overpowered by the hurt we kept inside, so strong it lost reason. It was wordless. *Look what you've done to me!* My deep-set eyes, my awkward shape bulging in the middle, my small shoulders, my matchstick legs… We ran out of ways to tell each other that we had no right to do what we had done. Our shape told our story.

Slowly, our claws relaxed into hands smooth with care. We sobbed spasmodically as the hurt stopped and started like a rusty old car until the engine died into an uncertain silence. Your care had once again cloaked my skin. Our cells interchangeable, our children ours, our hands steady and hate unafraid, we redefined our possessions. The love was there, and it mattered. We rested affirmed in that knowledge. We were not looking for a way back, just a way forward, just safe ways to test the newly emerging forms of affection. We knew that eventually we will forgive, and we will learn to smile at each other again over tablecloths, over cups of coffee, over soft tired heads of our children, hanging from our shoulders like all the transgressions we were given a chance to redeem.

begin again

the shroud of love lifts

          friends get tired of her mourning
          it's time to begin again

like a cuckoo
she rests her new-born dreams
with other people
until they start to grow
nurtured by the fire of their hearts

this year's harvest
was not plentiful
as left alone for too long
the dreams don't hatch

          they harden

living in opposition to you
her love had to be wild
tearing into her sides
shedding her old skin

         too soon

before the new skin
could sheathe her

she whispered names of men
she had loved before
but she was the only one reaching
asking them to give up something
a love

                      a home
                      a calling

to make her feel worthwhile again

and the men came
smelling the vulnerability
they never looked for her

                      but were glad

to have found her anyway

she wanted to rest in open arms
but had to uncover herself

                      to deserve it

afraid to look at them
she smiled so hard
her lips split her face

                      she hoped

to command respect
but breathed in lust instead
and her knees collapsed

over her daily wreckage of longing
she tensed her muscles
to resist involuntary compliance
so heavy like it was hers
while the world moved in traffic

                lightly
                unseeing her

it made her fingertips hum
when she touched your memory
and listened to your silence

she will not break it
for a step before she fell
was the most beautiful step ever taken

                and now

she will call things by their real names

reliving past hope
she begins again
one dinner at a time

                until

surprised by the touch
of another man's affection
she lies still
pressing into his old known heart
sinking into her quiet thoughts
afraid to scare the moment away
as his hands feel her beautiful

the one with regrets

Bangaluru, …

S he usually avoided travelling this far into herself, but he said:

"It could have been mine."

His words were laced with a faint trace of pain, it pulled them down and kept the rest of them in. He was trying to commit to memory her whole new body, one he had never seen before and probably wouldn't see again.

"I think it couldn't", she said rather abruptly. It made his fingers twitch with annoyance. He locked them together to keep himself composed.

Of course, she sensed it. She put her hand on his and spoke softly this time, surrendering the battle she did not want to fight. She had already won the war.

"You know I didn't mean it that way", she bent to find his eyes, to make sure he looked at her. She wanted to show that she knew he was being vulnerable and, as rare as these moments were, she wanted him to know he could share it. "It's just that... well. You had to believe in me to make me real."

He let out a sudden laugh. It sounded bland and so he stopped immediately. Instead, he stood up and looked down to the yard, filled with the morning sunlight. The family was away and so the yard was swarming with a different kind of life. He strained his ears to listen, but birds masked all the other sounds. It made him feel uneasy. Like a thief, he was stealing back to the past and caressing something which was no longer his - a soft, warm moment in a chaotic, raucous life. He will probably leave unnoticed, but at what cost to himself?

"Let's go inside."

She squirmed in her chair like the injustice of his thoughts sent a colony of ants up her arm:

"Wait a moment - you know I have no way out of this, right? I am pinned down. That is it. I can't even lift myself up! I am heavy, swollen from the inside. And even when I get my waist back," she added as he opened his mouth to interject, "I will still be responsible for a life, the first one ever other than my own. All my decisions from this point onward will be made for the greater common good. I might be good at it or might even like it, but I mourn it now. Now is the only time I have to mourn; I don't think there will be any later! So yes, there is no way back for me anymore."

She lifted one hand in front of his face to show him the turmeric-stained fingertips and short trimmed nails and laughed. She had been cooking. This means her life had already transformed irrevocably.

He smiled but she knew his discomfort and anger were still there, still tempting him to bolt and never come back. A bit like a dying animal, she thought. Men are such peculiar creatures.

She grabbed his hand and pulled it to her stomach. He jumped as if it burnt him, but she pulled him back in a practised gesture of those who kept a firm grasp on their life and their household. She knew what was needed in her radius of power. He was way too close to swallowing pain. As such, she knew what needed to be said.

"*He* made me swell," she emphasised the word to let him know that she understood where his anger placed the blame, "and I am not whole like I used to be. I am larger than my own love now. I am no longer in control. Now there is a part of me which is independent. I can't think for it. It has a mind and a will of its own. I don't know it, it's a stranger to me, I have not met it yet. It has a heart, unique and beating to its own rhythm."

Her voice turned sad as if she had talked herself into something uncomfortable, a well-laid trap. Her hand trembled lightly and moved to her belly with careful rounded tenderness as if telling the bulge not to listen.

He moved his hand slowly away from her so as not to offend her. He did not know the swell either. A tiny thing yet it completely transformed her. She was no longer his. Not even as a memory: her face drowned in a slew of imperfect moments he could no longer confidently piece together.

And that part will tear you and cause you pain. It will keep you awake and constantly worried. It will feed on you, and you will wither, he thought. *It will make you pale and restless, and yet you will keep it and cuddle it and kiss it. You will annihilate anyone who tries to harm it. You will give yourself away for it. And you will feel happy doing it.*

He ran his hand through his hair, pulling himself out of this melancholy, and looked down from the balcony again. The street beyond the garden was swarming with people, poisoning the edges of their green oasis with car horns and meaningless shouts.

"Let's go inside", he said again, hovering over her protectively. He tried to find somewhere to put his hands in order to support her. They felt empty.

She stood up. The effort to carry her waist stole her breath, quickly extinguishing a moan into a sigh:

"I'm fine, I'm fine, even these things one gets used to…"

He let her pass through the door and watched her crawl onto the bed on all fours, just like a tigress: feline, warm and vibrating with inner impulses. Fragile, inviting, and dangerous. A mature sensuality he had not seen in her before surrounded her now and he paused to acknowledge that he did not know this new woman.

She wrapped herself around her pregnant belly, an animal in pain. He ran his fingers across the bedsheet, so close to her but not daring to touch yet. It felt a lot like respect. Tired of feeling useless, he picked up a comb from the nightstand and ran it through her hair to detangle some of the night's worries and make it radiant again, cracking with positivity.

She cried. But just a little.

your child

Lithuania, …

where the houses are
shifting ghosts in the dark
guarding the sacred emptiness
devoured by the muted turn of snow
i scream deserts out of my lungs

a violently peaceful
winter safari

i made a vow to myself
when your wife's womb
overflows with new life
i will spread my legs and allow
my love to be consummated

        i felt heavy with the idea
        of a child

i cannot make light of these choices
that led me here
anchored to despair that gives life
like a quietly ripening miracle
i fight gravity in my lungs

        my body
        is a foreign country

the insides of my eyelids are cut
by distance
straight as a whip line
with the noon sunshine at its tip
but my toes are frosty

        i live
        in double time

you caress your baby
new and warm
awoken to brilliant sunlight
as the snowflakes slash the windscreen
in my cold desert
colliding with reality

             the presence of the unborn
             betrays me

             i dive under to tell you this

you caressed me unknowingly
as you were washing away
the sins of your day
from your hands
in a white hospital wing
with a light-hearted amen

but i am not your sin

             i am holy

night in the
sauna

Lithuania, …

crispy night in the sauna
women line benches like cats
stretching and folding
hissing at the slow steam
blowing out dead lovers

memory
tumbled with stone and fire
purified from pain
it scolds the night's surface
short-sighted
chipped like melting sugar crust
where the path on the frozen lake sits

they will stay in the heat
lazily naked
suggestively familiar
and if your desire will be the ladle
to crack open the sweetest parts
you will meet the morning
feeling whole again

and every girl sometimes cries in the sauna
and brain shatters harder than heart
and voice empties
trying to tell a stranger

                    that everyone
                    is always
                    someone
                    else's

the un-fairytale

Lithuania, …

can you just listen to my story
she screams
but he stifles her within himself
the sleeping beauty
in the prison of her head

only not as beautiful
only not entirely sleeping
only a water spirit

she wants to know
is there someone who collects pain
and listens to it like seashells

                    hurt to shyness

dreams flutter in her ears
to attack her from within
for she has too many ghosts
that mean something
their tails and claws stuck in her flesh
but the taste of you lingers
like the after-hope
on a blood-crusted seafoam

for the grass-snake king is dead[13]
and the morning fog
holds the wind from the crime scene

                    like a barricade tape

the lighthouse howls in the distance

how deep had she fallen
that nobody noticed her disappear
into the sound of crashing
a rag doll in the waves
it made the perpetrators quiver
until they turned into trees
salted

            twisted

                wood

---

13   reference to the Lithuanian folklore tale *Egle the Queen of Serpents*

birthed by the sea
into the hands of the wind

she found herself

in a moment of honesty
for the water reflected her image

but the tide moved
to soak her like tar
deeper than anger

it pushes into you too
until your eyes turn inward
conjuring melancholy
that smog

from beyond memory

and you know it is evil
when you catch yourself sinking
into quiet

dreamless

sleep

breathing scared
what is this darkness within me

the one in white

"Would you come and visit me if I was dying?"

I asked you this because I felt that starved with loneliness as I was, I would not live past 54. Maybe then your wife would allow you to see me in the open for once, to share with me a moment witnessed.

"I think so, but don't make me make promises," you answered.

I was not surprised. Things only happened when I made them to.

Just like you always feared, I got incredibly good at willing things into existence. But it was laborious pulling possibilities out of my navel, measuring them against each other to perfect the vision, and moulding them into reality. There were so many people to consider, their wishes contradicting each other, their actions making my clay futures crumble to dust. You see, I had not started dreaming early enough, when the story was still young and I was still the protagonist.

Time used to drape the narrative around me then. I did not like my odds so much anymore.

It was my heart that betrayed me, quivering through cold nights of slow solitude. Monitors cannot detect heartbreak, but it is a health condition nonetheless. I was told this is quite common, the most standard thing really, to have your heart ache but not shatter. Yet it developed a little hole. This little opening allowed other things to slip through: the visions, the melancholia, the naughty time that either ran or crawled but never paced itself to my heartbeat.

The stroke.

One evening I found myself in a white hospital bed, so much like one of those impersonal hotels we met at: anonymous, generic, aquatic in the sounds that filled the sterile space. Today it is me, tomorrow - someone else.

I picked up the phone and dialled your number.

My voice jerked you into reality. You ran into the bathroom to muffle the sound of the call, but you needn't have worried. It did not last long. Your wife did not even stir yet you knew you would have to wake her - a difficult conversation waited ahead. Crouched on the toilet seat in a crammed tiled space, your laptop screen humming aglow, you booked your flights.

Of course, she minded. She flew in with you but did not dare to come in. Worried sick, she replayed your silences in her head, imagining them turning into words, unlocked by my presence. She paced the room, took sleeping pills, and then walked them off in parks that lay unnaturally still, suffocated by the fog at sunrise. When you did not come back by the end of the next day, she called in.

I was long gone by then.

***

Do you remember a girl so isolated by her pain that bitterness would drown out her sorrow? She could not speak because she could not be heard. She could not speak because her words were too many and they doubled up, like bubbles from an asphyxiating fish. She held magic in her hands, and it tired her. She was trying relentlessly to live in double time in order to change your choices. But one cannot bend time without falling victim to it: if you pause your story, it pauses your heartbeat as it is left suspended with no lifeline left to count for. The sun rose twice for her that day and she died twice too, as if still unable to tell which timeline she belonged to.

It was a quiet tragedy in a loud hospital wing. Her life was overtaken by the machines just before it left with a modest sigh, and the shadows flew across the length of the room, deepening the white. It was marred by the stains left by souls that crashed through the walls without grace.

***

You did not feel anything when I died and that was what bothered you the most. You felt every little thing that happened in my life as if it happened inside you, but my death passed you like a dull and unremarkable thing. Terrified that you let this happen, you took a small gold ring from my hand to remember me by. Your wife flew out of the room, slamming the door in hurt as you transferred the ring from your pocket and onto your little finger. It grew into it, delicate branch patterns twisting deeper into your skin like roots, looking to quench their thirst in the tides of your pulse.

Your daughter watched you with questions in her eyes. There were some stories you owed your child, and she was about to claim them. She already knew love was more complicated than you wanted her to see.

Years later, she would toss in her bed, consumed by wordless worry. *Will it ever be possible to love just one person? Will I be as brave as life requires me to be?* To have love assigned and love chosen was a premise for a struggle that would also consume her heartbeats.

You spoke to your memories of me at night. Sometimes, overpowered by sleep, you said the words out loud, and they flew into the indifferent night. You were the misunderstood one, the rebel who never truly rebelled, and your family listened in pointed ignorance, allowing your consciousness to tip over and occasionally spill onto the dinner table. Uncovered, your old scars were weeping.

You aged in wooden chairs, hugged by the foliage, visited by the neighbourhood children, scavenging for sweets. It was a different world from the one you grew up in, knew or understood, but you talked to it all the same. You taught it to echo your words back at you in the sound of my voice from the time when it was still void of pain. In the final moments you whispered:

"Would you come visit me? I think I am dying."

nomad

what does this white girl know
of *sambar*[14]
or of the sunny fields
with women and children
with pounding of the stone mortar
and soup
served in a banana leaf

this white girl is lonely

what does this white girl know
of *idli*[15]
or of fruit
ripe with honest sweetness
or of chickens and goats
a tin roof
and red dust between your toes

this white girl is shivering

---

14 a meal, traditional to South Indian cuisine
15 a meal, traditional to South Indian cuisine

what does this white girl know
of *sadya*[16]
or of rickshaws zooming past
van slogans
car horns
and fish markets
and a street preacher on a ramp
sending faith into the madding crowd

this white girl was born

                    into steepled silence

and what does this white girl know
of joy
or family
or taste of sacrifice
of stew or curry or spice
she borrowed it once and took it back
she folded laughter away
she was polite
even though she was not free
from longing

this white girl

         is slowly disintegrating

                into chaos

she cooks and feasts

             alone

looking for a trace of sun in her belly
like a chicken looks
for a grain of gold

---

16   a meal, traditional to South Indian cuisine

the one where
nothing changes

Exeter, ...

My house had a heartbeat. It echoed in the pipes, pushing out water in stalling gushes and puffing steam on unsuspecting passers-by from its probing boiler tubes. At 4am, the gas meter would start with a gentle tuk-tuk, dropping the third beat into silence. Then the door from the veranda would swing open, knocking against the radiator, echo launching into the space, startled by the audacity of its own volume. The house was a living organism. It pulled me out of sleep sighing and creaking like an old, tired ghost crawling the floors, sniffing, and purring to warm me into consciousness just as you started your day.

I did not have a cat. There were no plants in the windows. I did not fill this house like the belly of the whale; while others set their space like tiny doll houses, controlled and clean, with airbrushed kisses and miniature parlours designed for homely lives, mine felt emptier with every passing year. The older I got, the fewer things I needed. I was always packed to leave, never settled in one place, never completely returned.

While my house waited like a trusty pet with soppy eyes, overwhelmed with too much space, I hid above the clouds, where my life felt mine again. The time spent there was immeasurable, flying in between time zones with sun under my wings. The past was alive, and the future had not happened yet. There I felt the strength coming back into my limbs, my veins filling up with abundant life, so strong it scared me. My soul had stayed too long in a lifeless wasteland, and I started to wind it back into my chest, feeling the intoxicating compulsion to grow and live within me again. I yearned to be a conscious participant in my choices, intentional and deliberate, and to reimagine my life in breath-taking colour, excited for what was to come.

And when you come - from beyond the sunrise, your skin charged with warm glow - the windows of my house will blow open to call you in. The light will dance back onto the abandoned floorboards and the dust will lift from the empty rooms. The dreams will stir and slither out from behind the wallpaper to greet their master. They were too wild, the world tripped over their inconvenience and got angry, so we have stowed our dreams in the shelter of anonymous papery shadows. Slow and sleepy, these forgetful ghosts made space for our memories.

It will be beautiful, like a movie, having you here, stuck with me in a finite timeline. The light will settle on the heavy kitchen counter, and wooden chairs with carved tops will assume their rightful place in hungry corners. I will roll the dough for your coffee sweets, and you will bend me over the flour, spread luxuriously for a moment of ecstasy in a white dusty sun beam. It will go on, again and again, like a simulation of something that has happened somewhere once before, until we grow slow and tired of love making.

I looked at my watch and saw that time was a circle. If only I had found where it began, I would have grabbed and pulled to unravel it like yarn from a spindle. I would have undone the work of fate and returned it to the clouds of wool to be combed and loved into a new life.

But the law of time is clear — the stubborn will be broken. The hand of seconds snatches my breath and runs away. I can feel my bones bending to reach for the tentative touches of impermanent peace. When she is done with her work, what will there be left to recall?

I rewind the movie of our lives and cry at all the right moments.

When you come, I will set the table with flowers of reconciliation and dishes of guilt. They will leave coffee stains on your tongue. We will feast with doors locked to keep the time out. Then we will part until the next time when the hunger for dreams once lost overwhelms us and we meet to pull them out of our mouths, once again upsetting the gravity.

thoughtful ignorance

you love him don't you now
too many years have passed
and you got used to him
to the point of affection

you wonder sometimes
how does he see you
a lover or a wife
is his emotion

a genuine compromise
love is never wild here
but in the distant centre
of someone else's dream
sun burns circles
into their desire
and streets steal men
between work and home
looking to find

affection
that is not prescribed but homemade
affection
that is exotic to their promises
affection that seeks out
hard nipples in wet sarees
and drips through their fingertips
in quivering residues of longing

they sin from within
but lock desire
like a cuckoo in the clock
when they step back
into the absent-minded order
of their trusting home
momentarily creaseless

thoughts trickle into you
in the privacy of your shower
but they leave no trace
and you know he is yours forever
so why would you try
to find out otherwise

the one where he makes his move

Exeter, ...

Some things are private to our souls. You should not try to extract them into words, for they would get stuck in your throat or stumble out with the wrong intonation stripping them of their purity. These things are always already in the open, written in the tension under the skin, and you can see them if you know how to look.

Silly woman, the truth jumped in front of you while you were unprepared to see it.

His phone was ringing. It jolted me from my wonderful delusion. This parallel life was not the dream we wanted; it did not make us happy. Nor did it exist as dreams usually exist when others are allowed to see them. In the eye of the beholder – the bellboy, the poolside stranger, the guard – we were not what we were. To them, we were lucky: the breakers of metal tasting tradition, the unspeakable caught being wildly in love, the object of jealousy, the confirmation of untold possibilities. They smiled, oblivious of our true position: the dream gone stale and stained with guilt like your grandmother's moth-eaten lace curtains.

I looked at the number, picked it up and said 'hello' in my morning voice, telling of warm sheets and sleepy breath before coffee. I was met with silence. Chopped by the turn of the fan, the distant background voices continued on the other end of the line, but the caller was calculating whether she had entered the wrong number. With a relaxed familiarity of someone who decided to stay in control, I said to the woman I had never spoken to before:

"Are you going to say something?"

She did not and her silence put on a decisive edge. I hung up and placed the phone back on the bedside table, then sat up with a new sense of resolution. It was not me to be the bearer of sorrow, the reinforcer of jungle laws, but I jumped to the opportunity so easily, as if I was born for it.

Eat or be eaten.

I headed to the bathroom to start my day. He was still in the shower, and I stepped in to place a kiss on his back. The seed was sown. From the underbelly - the parallel universe of sterile hotel rooms and pretend luxury - here I rose to the daylights of real-life sorrows, joys, and guilt, of beauty that smells fresh even if it fades quickly. There was no telling anymore what this new day would bring.

Crazed with pain, you packed your bag in an instant. You picked your daughter up to focus yourself, but each time you laid her head on your shoulder she would melt your defences and tears would come, leaving you helpless. Helplessness forged your spirit and the way only the helpless can do, you saw your situation with exceptional clarity. You have not been working for a couple of years now. You did not want to take a break, but you also loved your baby. He managed all the money. You did not want to talk to anyone about what had just revealed itself to you, but you also could not stay. You called your brother and the tremor in your voice instructed his hand. Next morning you and your baby were on the plane to your parents. You did not leave a note. You blocked his number.

I had always wondered how it was going to happen. Would he drop onto one knee, wrapped in the soft night lights? Would we hide in shame for my rounded belly and whisper vows, eyes down, telling ourselves they are as sincere now as ever? Or would we be too old to want anything else but honest companionship then? One thing was constant: I always wanted him to choose me by his own will, for me, not because I fit into his family, his schedule, his environment, but because I mattered.

When did that change?

Here he was with me, having nowhere else to go.

He called your house continuously for two days until your parents shamed you into speaking to him. He did not deny anything, he did not explain it either. You did not ask any questions. You had already felt the truth and he respected you enough not to lie. You did bring a child to this world together, and although now you hated the idea of sharing her with him, you had to set your pain aside for her. You made it perfectly clear that you would not be coming back to him though.

He closed himself off for a year. Could he believe he had his life back? A man, having once felt suppressed, found himself at a loss with the freedom he no longer desired. He felt desperate to stop this change but at the same time the unspeakable prospect of moving away and disappearing from his old life made him oddly happy, albeit ashamed and hesitant to admit it. He stayed away from people as much as he could while he tried to unravel the complex knot of emotions attacking him from within. He felt like a man dwarfed by fate, trying to rebuild a house with nothing but a toy toolbox - a demoralising task even without the overinvested spectatorship. In these parts of the world, it was customary to care about someone else's tragedy far beyond expectations of reasonable politeness. To avoid the predatory audience, he hid his conflicting thoughts in the company of plain apartment walls to feel his way through the events and arrange his next steps.

When he came, I was prepared for a fight, but he did not say anything to spark it. Did he realise that his misfortune was custom made? Hurt and unwilling to stay completely alone, he decided to give his crippled dream a chance. He did not bring flowers or a ring but brought himself, tired and dizzy with change. He could not ask the question. Instead, he laughed and made small talk, stringing words together that sounded strange to his ears, but would not go in until he had his answer. That evening he collapsed in my bed and thought with a sleep-clouded surprise that he managed to change everything about his life but none of it changed how he felt about himself.

I did not wear white, and we did not go to church. The innocence of our connection had been tainted and so there was no need for a celebration. There were no other witnesses apart from two confused friends who looked uncomfortable with their predicament. In the space of a week, I left my job, packed my life, and followed him.

This is what you get for saying yes to a man who told you his mouth already knew the taste of deceit. Does it really come as a surprise? But you did not have to say yes. He did not kneel to you in a moment of blissful vulnerability, choosing you was not a gesture of sincere devotion. His parents kneeled for him, and it was not done before you either. For me, he kneeled because I forced him to, and the innocence of romance died on the spot like a deer in the taillights.

His spirit was still his own, he never bowed to either of us.

He was not happy when you remarried. He never knew how to let go and for him you still felt like a part of his body. Or maybe he left a part of him within yours and it was that part that dragged his mind across continents. He knew you inside out, but now so did someone else.

And the child? She was lucky to have two whole families, they said. But he knew that instead of providing her with certainty he was making her choose: which parent is your favourite? Would you like to stay with mommy or daddy this holiday? She was choosing without a choice as she could never have both of them be there for her for long enough to piece a life out of it.

How do you describe to a child who the woman replacing her mother by the side of her father is? How do you explain that this woman does not hate her, she just loathes herself?

I knew it was bitterness that melted away the everyday structures of his first marriage, making space for me to step in, and I was afraid. We threw our lives together hastily, without time to prepare our minds, and the result was domestic uncertainty: we were not sure what we expected of each other or whether we even had the right to expect anything. Desperate for some stability, I wished to tell him that I was pregnant. A baby boy from a dream I once had, summoned to mark a new beginning. Would it be enough to crumble his sadness and make him carve out a space in his thoughts for me?

But the days went by without such news; they were instead sliced by work and food and television. I was no longer the invisible wallpaper ghost that ruffled tablecloth and sat on his knees during football broadcasts. He wished to but he could no longer deny I was there. We had something to live towards before, and now that the goal had been achieved, we forgot how it felt to want for something and be happy for the things yet to come. There was only time, and the to-do lists we wrote to avoid its endlessness.

We would argue after he went to see her, and I would retreat further into my self-imposed sense of alienation. He would roam the rooms, a stranger in his own house, and I would stay out of his way to allow him space to comprehend the unique state of loneliness he had pushed himself into. He turned his world around to feel happier, and yet still he would only smile genuinely when he interacted with his child. They understood each other effortlessly, tied by blood and the sacrifice of her birth which brought him hope. There was no space for me in between them, yet I was never asked to go away either. They had each other, and as long as that was there, everyone else flitted in and out of their company without making a lasting mark.

It dawned on me then that things happened for a reason. It was essential to let them take their shape and keep the memories pressed down so that they would not attempt to bubble up unexpectedly and conquer the land I was standing on. I had put my foot in the door and the door would not close anymore, leaving a constant draft. Would I not question – spending the rest of my life living out a memory – whether there was someone else for me in the present time, someone fashioned for the current me rather than asking me to rewind myself to fit the picture? Would I have been a different person with them, a different companion to them? I was reliving the dystopian version of my dream, trying to discover who I was as a person alone, having no hand to hold despite closing my eyes next to him every night.

She stepped out of her world like a witch. She went from being in love and wanting to be loved to only wishing for the mechanics of showing it. Being with a man subduing himself with alcohol, she could not rebuild the sense of value, just perpetually produce actions that once upon a time she knew to have had meaning. She was tied to her pain by the ring she forced onto her hand. She did not know how to release herself from it. She discovered that she was after all the blacksmith and not the mystical breaker of chains she once believed herself to be.

She shot herself in the head because it was the thoughts she was trying to let go of. They slid down her face like they were water -

until there were none.

still-life

monster
father

                                     hurting man

he sits
his little girl at his side
suckling her milk bottle
trust in the bend of her leg
sand-stained nappy
nestling with ripening skin

two ancients
hunching in sepia hues
watching over the world
like they have seen
that stretch of land
in the speck of light
in the foam kissed rocks

their colour
running like quicksand
sweet moments dripping
through their fingertips
sticky calm staining them
until they morph
into driftwood

a no lovingly spoken

my love for you is not embarrassing
i should be able to express it
even if you cannot accept it
it is a gift
and you know what they say about gifts
returning them breaks something
a link
a trust
a kindness

                  and suddenly

a heart

so i should be allowed
to message you i miss you
for a reply to come in two weeks' time
without you feeling guilty
or me sad

and i should be allowed
to kiss you on the cheek

or nose

or chin

when we both know i settled
or hug you tightly
confidently
only because it soothes me
without you growing bitter
but growing into me
because you've always liked it anyway

it makes me feel good
when you say hi sometimes
and it is such a small thing to do
to make me genuinely smile

a little

i should be most of all allowed
to tell you how i feel
as often as i need to
because it is your doing too
and you can help by saying
i'm grateful for these words
i will carry them with pride
even if i cannot
give you mine

you committed yourself to me
the day you invited me to share a moment

even though it was a long way to loving me
and i forgave you the day i decided to
even though it was a long way
until i let you feel it

so we
should be allowed
to do this without pain

and i should
be able to accept your no

                softly
               lovingly spoken

for my love is not embarrassing
it will leave me
when it's ready
to find home
in someone else

endings

—◆—

the one where life moves beyond
the story,

and it is ok

this story holds
your name

..., ...

From fragments of you and shards of me I wrote this story. I told you to listen once, and you stayed: grudgingly, unforgivingly, scared. Your pain, your craze, your anger when you were cornered by pieces of the past stole your voice, but you still read, feeling your fingers trace the edge of my bittersweet insanity. These are just words, alone they have no meaning. But there is magic running in my blood, and when I connect them, entire worlds arise fresh again.

I dreamt up our future, but it fell to the same conclusions. I hope we share peace in their aftertaste.

Do not get angry with me. I have said goodbye to you in so many ways already. I now ask you to forgive me this last one. It comes winged with gratitude. I look at you - strong and proud of what you have accomplished in love - and I cannot help but admire you. How you show care for your wife and child has become an inspiration to me. And a lesson of love. I have learnt from you the true weight of the bricks that go into the walls of your home, the aching the daily toil of building affection from the ground up leaves in your shoulders. But the fruits of it are sweet. I see them in your life, and they become real to me too. I hope to lace my own tongue with this sweetness one day.

Your skin is rich with experiences. It holds everything you have been through: your pain, your pride, all the sunny afternoons, the life-giving lessons spreading in a trail of sinews on your arms, and my love, growing fainter with every passing year like the colour on sun-facing walls. It will remain there, the structure holding up your nature, written into your name. Be proud of bearing it, you, who have been entrusted with the love of so many. Be happy, for it is love that has grown to be your beautiful burden. Love that is dirty, obscure, rebellious, uncomfortable, and brave, that defies structure and ignores reason, that heals and is magically simple.

We held onto it stubbornly, but not because we wanted to hurt anyone. We did this because the world hurt us and we felt we deserved to cause a moment of chaos on our way to complicity. We then bowed our heads, holding tenderly onto this memento - a thread of peace we forged in disruption.

So do not look back and let the fear of loss overwhelm you again. Do not let the old echoes of shame and guilt quietly seep into your dreams like the night sounds of the jungle, smuggled in by the fragrant summer air. This story has now been laid to rest. The tapestries of time hang empty, the ghosts of old disappointments have been freed from their tired folds.

Once we are old, I will call you by your name and you will come to me. It will be the time past all sacrifices. We will stand together, rooting into each other like tired woods, and the wind in our leaves will be breathing gratitude as it stills to make space for the heedless rains. They will run away with the memory of our troubles, leaving the streets fresh and clean for the generations to come.

i listen to your silence speak

i listen to your silence speak
in corridors that whisper madness
hiding actions committed
against wishes held dear
once

peace is invasive
sat in the armchairs of hope
that forgot how to reach
sacrificed for convenience
out of habit

you unroll the carpet of time
to reveal its ugly folds
for the chance to iron them out
but they crumble to the same conclusions
unashamed

you stole my voice to hide this story
but my words remained
breaking the cords to climb
to the light they deserved
unnamed

justice

it ought to have been difficult
to forget the quivering of injustice

it stretched behind me like a shadow
elongating my longing
drowning my steps in heavy reasoning
stuffy with lost chance of reproach

but the more i cried for justice
turning to the past
winding time in

the more it pulled me ahead
like a startled mare
as it tried to run forth
to unsettle
the sands of my future

and hope
oh hope

it unravelled in front of me
a robe never meant to be beautiful
threads tugging at me
the longer i chose to walk
deeper into the loss
with my back on home
and my face in the dying light

dreamless

they sit dreamless in hard wooden chairs
hands dried up and twisted like roots
growing into the structure
softened by the touch of time
words fall through cracks in their memory
their tongues deprived of action

                    speak only nouns

like a broken record
etching a single word
into the falling rhythm

they recall
myths about their own lives

                  the orange groves
                  the savannahs
                  the foxes

the love that flowed
between the soil and the stalk
to secure the lifeline
of this story

the guards of memory
too old to be opposed
they breathe
marinated history into the future

her eyes decrust
and while the myths flow
the frost retreats
until the old can stand again
and walk out holding hands
towards the exhausted woods
footsteps blown to dust
in the cricket silence
of the afternoon

the children will wonder
what has become of them
those elders with etched hands
but they were there to witness
only the moment was too private
and they dared not look at it

to my Friends

…, …

the pain i write has run out

it shed the skin like old slippers
rested on the linden-tree
until the context dried out
scales ruffling in the wind

it left me weak and shivering

children will watch it aghast
in their imagination
it will cultivate darkness

i lay in the wooden tub skinless
haunted by visions
of ancient rights and wrongs

            raw and bruised
            afraid to get up

for i would leave a mark on this world
as my trembling blood
would not settle easily

friends
you came in my hour of need
you surrounded me
with your corporal presence

            hands braced
            eyes watching outwards

you combed the fields with your bodies
feet planted in wet soil
driving the monsters away

            candles melting
            crickets falling
            whispers pouring
            you guarded me
            waiting for my skin to grow

ghostless

broken heart is a disease of the body
as much as of the soul

i find myself tossing feverishly
in the bed i obsess over making
every morning
aspiring to creaseless certainty
chasing after manic thoughts
that run
with wings of air-born dreams
until i burn them out
run them in
and sacrifice them
back into the cotton clouds

i have sectioned this loss from my body
and the hollow i now ache with
is finally ghostless

nine stories

the cat slipped out of the bag
and tiptoed up up up
like a cloud of warm dreams

the cat did not have nine lives
she lived nine stories
they were not stages of anything
just naturally hers to enter
once her first life got cut short
and she walked on determinately
the way bad news usually does
believing that the end
will never end her

don't try to hide the cat again
bags cannot contain
the sequence of events
she will pass through your life
without stopping
not giving you much thought
not sad or cold or hungry

not pleading to be taken in
just showing you answers to questions
you did not know you had

don't worry if it hurts you some
it is only the nature of things
like stars becoming black holes
like lava or gravity
and i wasn't a cat person either
before i cried after you
and she passed by showing me
that the dead can also walk

and now - thank you

and now

she does not write but linger over pages

committing her own story to memory

the mad woman

the promiscuous bard

indecent in her sincerity

she follows the beam of her desk lamp

and cuts herself off
from these empty humming spaces

and then
writing was a messy affair
eyes dark with whirlpools of desire
anxiety like a pressure cooker
ejecting splinters of her soul
to thrash about in the aeroplane void
dangerously close to indifference

pain was a private matter
it embarrassed the world to see it

the sweeper of visions
the duster of hope
the silence herself
with fragile fingers
she will rise
strong and tender
a newborn to this land
with hands ready to grow into it
by the airport exit sign
stepping into the light of life
and melting
into this moment
sensual
and fully lived

and now
she is so incredibly proud of you

happiness is a heavy word to hold
and you have grown heavy with it
exhaustion does not drive you away
nor do dangerous eyes
or hearts that could be persuaded
you do not cause devotion to recoil
in home-grown hurt
but hold the sky in place for so many
your chest a pillar
growing larger with life
each time the pulsing web of hands
expands around you
like a breath
elastic
with a quiet thank you

this house is now
a home

my future, now

this house is now a home
and the stale wallpaper
thick with moth-eaten silences
endured on many sharp days
has peeled away
revealing soft white purity

the light lingers lovingly
on a blossoming bouquet of flowers
real
heavy with nectar
hypnotising sleepy bees to hover
like ghostly generals of tired battles
dusting from under their tender wings
a faint taste of mellow evening

my lips blow
onto a spoonful of curry
to calm it down
to relieve its entitled anger
for this dish is too young to understand
the meanings cooked into it

it will be passed on
to an expectant mouth of a child
and my voice will fill the space
with myths like steady river
cooling after the heat
calling forth the ones
who love the deep

and after
when i wonder the house
putting it to sleep
with the ritual of my footsteps
the careless mirror shows my face
back at me

and i look happy
without even noticing

the end

Read it?
Love it?
Hate it?
Rate it!
On Goodreads
and Amazon x

acknowledgments

My heart-felt thanks goes to Christine Rahman and Holly Govey, my friends who gave their time to read my work and encouraged me along the way.

about the author

Kristina V. Kairyte Kristina is a Lithuanian born emigree who moved to the UK to study literature and film. Kristina holds an MA in English and Film Studies from the University of Exeter. She is currently working in media.

This is Kristina's first book.

Printed in Great Britain
by Amazon

20584517R00119